03716594

GW00385417

THE PHOTOGRAPHIC WORK OF

# CALVERT RICHARD JONES

ROLLIN BUCKMAN

WITH AN INTRODUCTION BY

JOHN WARD

SCIENCE MUSEUM

*LONDON* HER MAJESTY'S STATIONERY OFFICE

First published 1990

ISBN 0 11 290462 9

British Library Cataloguing in Publication Data
*A CIP catalogue record for this book is available from the British Library*

HMSO publications are available from:

**HMSO Publications Centre**
(Mail and telephone orders only)
PO Box 276, London, SW8 5DT
Telephone orders 01–873 9090
General enquiries 01–873 0011
(queuing system in operation for both numbers)

**HMSO Bookshops**
49 High Holborn, London, WC1V 6HB 01–873 0011 (Counter service only)
258 Broad Street, Birmingham, B1 2HE 021–643 3740
Southey House, 33 Wine Street, Bristol, BS1 2BQ (0272) 264306
9–21 Princess Street, Manchester, M60 8AS 061–834 7201
80 Chichester Street, Belfast, BT1 4JY (0232) 238451
71 Lothian Road, Edinburgh, EH3 9AZ 031–228 4181

**HMSO's Accredited Agents**
(see Yellow Pages)

*and through good booksellers*

# CONTENTS

# PREFACE

The catalogue contained in this book systematically records over 400 different images photographed nearly 150 years ago by Calvert Richard Jones. Where attribution is questionable, this has been noted; it is hoped that there are no serious omissions and that the catalogue will serve as a source for future research in the history of photography. I have through this study come to appreciate both the true artistic talents and the perseverance which led Calvert Richard Jones to produce so many calotypes of such beauty.

ROLLIN BUCKMAN

# ACKNOWLEDGMENTS

Dr Roderick Howell, Hon Curator of Art, Royal Institution of South Wales; William C Rogers, genealogist and historian; and Dr David Painting, Hon Curator of Photography, Royal Institution of South Wales, gave valuable assistance and support during my initial research in Swansea. Iwan Meical Jones and Colin Lacy encouraged me with their interest in this project. Mike Weaver and Sean Thackrey shared their knowledge of nineteenth-century photography. Mrs Harrison D Horblit and Hans P Kraus, Jr, generously opened their collections for study, and museum directors, curators and their assistants gave of their time and expertise that this catalogue might be as comprehensive as possible. I wish to thank Brian Coe of the Royal Photographic Society; Michael Gibbs, President of the Royal Institution of South Wales; Colin Harding of the National Museum of Photography, Film and Television; Robert Lassam, Curator of the Fox Talbot Museum; Christopher Titterington, Department of Designs, Prints and Drawings, Victoria and Albert Museum; and particularly John Ward, Curator of Photography and Cinematography Collections, Science Museum, for believing that this catalogue should be published. Finally, I express my greatest appreciation to Virginia, my wife, who assisted me in every step of the research.

# SOURCES OF ILLUSTRATIONS AND ENTRIES

The images included and/or referenced are from the following collections: their permission to reproduce is gratefully acknowledged.

David Alan Brown, Washington DC; George Eastman House, Rochester, New York; The JP Getty Museum, California; Glynn Vivian Art Gallery, Swansea Museum Services, Swansea City Council; Martyn Gregory Gallery, London; Robert Hirshkowitz Ltd, London; Harrison D Horblit, Connecticut; Dr Roderick G Howell, Swansea; Andre Jammes, Paris; Hans P Kraus Jr, New York; Lacock Abbey Museum, Lacock; Colin Lacy Gallery, London; National Library of Wales, Aberystwyth; National Maritime Museum, Greenwich; National Museum of Photography, Film and Television, Bradford; Princeton University, The Art Museum, New Jersey; Royal Institution of South Wales Photographic Collection, Swansea; Royal Library of Copenhagen, Denmark; Royal Photographic Society, Bath; Science Museum, London; Smithsonian Institution, Washington DC; Swansea Central Reference Library; Sotheby's, London; Victoria and Albert Museum, London

# INTRODUCTION

## *W H Fox Talbot, Calvert Richard Jones and the Calotype Decade*

JOHN WARD

In March 1839 William Henry Fox Talbot received a letter from a cousin by marriage in Wales which contained a scribbled addition. The letter began 'Dear Talbot, The writer of the above queries is a friend of your cousins' & quite beside himself on the subject of your photogenic researches. He pressed one so much to communicate with you that I consented to do so – reluctantly – because I know to what an extent you must be overwhelmed with inquiries'. The additional lines read: 'The *exact* proportions between the salt and water, and between the nitrate of silver and water which he considers best. And the time between repeating the washings which produce the greatest sensitivity'. This note was signed 'Calvert R. Jones' and dated 8 March 1839.[1] Talbot, the recipient of the note, had recently announced one of the most significant inventions of the age, the negative-positive photographic process. The Reverend Calvert Richard Jones was to be one of the most enthusiastic practitioners of the new art of photography and, for three years, one of Talbot's closest collaborators in his efforts to exploit his invention commercially.

William Henry Fox Talbot was a remarkable man. In 1839, although still more than a year away from his fortieth birthday, he was already a Fellow of the Royal Society with twenty-nine scientific or mathematical papers to his name. He had been educated at Harrow and Cambridge where he was an outstanding scholar. At Cambridge, Talbot had taken the mathematical tripos which gave him a solid grounding in mathematics and physics, but his scientific interests were wide-ranging and included astronomy, botany and chemistry. Science was not his only preoccupation, for he was also deeply interested in the classics, etymology and philology. Talbot was briefly a Liberal Member of Parliament but very quickly found politics not to his taste.

Figure 1 William Henry Fox Talbot by John Moffat, 1864. Fox Talbot Collection, Science Museum, London.

Talbot was an only child of upper-class parents. His father died within six months of the young Talbot's birth, but his mother remarried four years later and he acquired two half-sisters. Talbot did not succeed to his first father's estate until 1821 and was not able to take over the family home, Lacock Abbey in Wiltshire, until 1826. As a consequence he spent much of his youth at the homes of relations elsewhere in Wiltshire, and at Penrice on the Welsh coast near Swansea. The bonds formed during this period were strong and enduring. Throughout his lifetime he visited and corresponded with the Welsh branch of his family. They in turn were enthusiastic supporters of Talbot's work and passed on much of their enthusiasm and knowledge to their friends, one of whom was Calvert Jones.

The story of Talbot's discovery of a practical photographic process is well documented. His failure to produce satisfactory sketches with two popular artist's aids of the period, the camera lucida and camera obscura, provided the stimulus which began his investigations. Talbot was led to the idea that instead of laboriously tracing with a pencil the detailed scenes captured by these instruments, he might instead coat paper with a light-sensitive silver salt and record them chemically. After repeated experiments Talbot began to achieve promising results and by the spring of 1834 he was making 'distinct and pleasing images of such things as leaves, lace, and other flat objects of complicated forms'.[2] No instrument was used to make these images. The original artifacts were simply placed on sheets of paper sensitised with silver salts and exposed to sunlight. Talbot's first experiments with the camera obscura were unsuccessful and it was only later that he was able to make camera pictures. (The earliest surviving such camera image dates from August 1835.) During the autumn of 1834 Talbot seems to have discovered at least one means of preserving or 'fixing' his images, more or less permanently. In February 1835 Talbot had recorded the intriguing observation that the lights and shades of his pictures were reversed. Furthermore, by using one of these reversed images as an original to be placed on his sensitive paper, Talbot found that any number of pictures could be produced in which the lights and shades were represented normally.[3] These were momentous discoveries. The use of a fixed negative to produce an unlimited number of positive prints is the basis of modern photography.

At this time Talbot seems to have set no great store on his photographic investigations, for he made no attempt to publicise his discoveries and only a small circle of his family and friends knew anything of his work. It was not until January 1839 that he published details of his invention. The event which spurred him into action was the announcement of an incredible discovery by a Frenchman, Louis Jacques Mandé Daguerre, for capturing the images found by the camera obscura which 'confounds all the theories of science in light and optics'.[4] Talbot hastened to show examples of his own work at London's prestigious Royal Institution and submitted a paper to the Royal Society which was read on 31 January.[5] Talbot was, naturally, keen to establish priority for his own discovery, and not solely for the sake of his personal reputation. Britain and France were fierce trade rivals and memories of the Napoleonic wars were still fresh in many minds on both sides of the Channel. In a letter to *The Literary Gazette* published on 2 February 1839, Talbot lamented his 'mischance' that having 'devoted much labour and attention to the perfecting of this invention' he was forestalled by the announcement of the French discovery. In fact, Talbot seems to have carried out no substantial work on photography since his experiments in 1835 and it is difficult to sympathise with his complaint. His mother, Lady Elizabeth Feilding, bitterly disappointed that her only son had let possible fame and fortune pass him by, wrote acidly on 3 February 'This is *at least* the second time the same sort of thing has happened',[6] and again, 'I shall be v. glad if M. Daguerre's invention is proved to be v. different from yours'.[7] Talbot's rather sheepish reply two days later contained the admission 'it appears that . . . M. Daguerre's experiments were prior to mine. I have received a letter from M. Biot [a French scientist] . . . he is able to attest that M. Daguerre has been occupied on the subject for 14 years'.[8]

Talbot was not to know it at the time but Daguerre's process was very different from his own. The French process produced a direct positive image on copper plates thinly coated with silver which had been made light-sensitive by iodine vapour. The images, called daguerreotypes (see fig 2), were finely detailed but could only be duplicated with difficulty. Talbot's images on paper were coarse and crude by comparison but his negative-positive technique (fig 3) allowed him to produce an unlimited number of copies. Both processes required long exposure times, and photographs of any living or moving subject were impossible. The announcement of the two rival photographic processes aroused tremendous public interest

Figure 2 Daguerreotype portrait by Richard Beard, c1843. Science Museum, London.

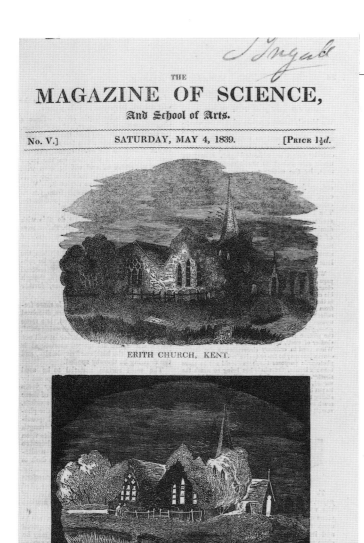

THE

MAGAZINE OF SCIENCE,

And School of Arts.

No. V.] SATURDAY, MAY 4, 1839. [PRICE 1½d.

ERITH CHURCH, KENT.

FAC-SIMILE OF PHOTOGENIC DRAWING.

Figure 3 Title page of the *Magazine of Science*, 4 May 1839, showing Talbot's negative-positive process. Science Museum, London.

and enthusiasm. Because few details of Daguerre's process were published there was inevitable muddle and confusion in the press, and much crude chauvinism. Talbot did publish some details of his process, which he had called photogenic drawing, but he perhaps made the mistake of making it seem too simple. He suggested in his letter to *The Literary Gazette* that the picture made itself: 'All that the artist does is to dispose the apparatus before the object whose image he requires: he then leaves it for a certain time, greater or less, according to circumstances. At the end of the time he returns, takes out his picture, and finds it finished'.

Unfortunately it was not as easy as that, as the many would-be photographers who rushed out to try this wonderful new discovery soon found out. In 1839, photogenic drawing was a difficult and inconsistent art and only the most patient and persistent were likely to enjoy any success. There were many calls in the press, and privately to Talbot, along the same lines as Calvert Jones's note, asking for more precise details. As Robert Hunt, a distinguished photographic experimenter later remarked,

> *The photographic processes appeared, when first reported, to be so simple that most persons conceived they could procure, without trouble, specimens of equal beauty with those exhibited by the artist and the philosopher . . . It requires but the slightest consideration to convince us, that an element inappreciably subtile [sic], must, in its action on chemical preparations, be affected by the most trifling change; and that differences beyond detection by any other test, would become glaringly evident under the influence of light.*[9]

The difficulties were too great for many and they abandoned the art, including Calvert Jones, who turned his attentions to the daguerreotype process.

Talbot was aware that his process had many imperfections and in several respects compared unfavourably with Daguerre's. This became even more apparent in August 1839 when details of the French invention were published and the first specimens were made in England. Although Talbot worked hard to improve photogenic drawing throughout 1839 and 1840, and received some gratifying reviews of his work in the press, it was the minutely detailed daguerreotypes that began to capture public imagination. The daguerreotype process was also capable of improvement and many were working in both Europe and America to increase the sensitivity of the plates and thus shorten exposure times. Talbot must have been particularly worried when towards the end of 1839 his French correspondent, Biot, wrote to him of another new photographic process on paper devised by Hippolyte Bayard,[10] but he did not let this deflect him from his own experiments.

It was in September 1840 that he finally made the discovery that was to transform his art. When making photogenic drawings it was necessary to expose sensitised paper in a camera until an image appeared, a procedure that could take from twenty minutes to an hour. Talbot discovered that a much briefer exposure produced an invisible or latent image which could be made visible, or 'developed', with a solution of gallic acid. The consequences were dramatic. Exposure times were reduced to a few minutes, immeasurably broadening the scope of Talbot's technique. Most importantly, he could now photograph living subjects. Talbot called his new process the calotype (also known as the Talbotype) and, like Daguerre, went on to patent his process in England. By the end of 1840 it was clear that both processes were ripe for commercial exploitation, and portrait photography seemed to have the most immediate economic potential. In Britain, however, the two processes were to develop down rather different paths – they were exploited, broadly, by rather different people, and enjoyed rather different levels of success.

The first daguerreotype portrait studio in Europe was opened in March 1841 in London's Regent Street. The proprietor was Richard Beard, an entrepreneur and one-time coal merchant. His studio was an immediate success. Beard opened two further studios in 1842 and is reputed to have made between £25,000 and £35,000 in that year alone.[11] Within months of the opening of Beard's first studio, Antoine Claudet, a Frenchman living in England, had opened a rival daguerreotype portrait establishment on the roof of the Adelaide Gallery in London. Soon such studios became one of the age's fashionable successes. By the end of the decade almost every community in Britain boasted at least one daguerreotypist and in the

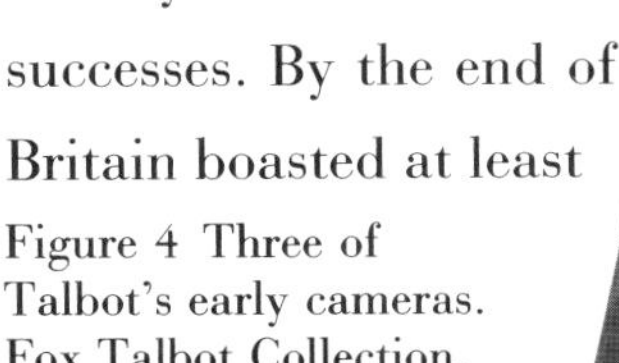

Figure 4 Three of Talbot's early cameras. Fox Talbot Collection, Science Museum, London.

major towns and cities there were many competitors.

At the outset, people who took up daguerreotype photography as a profession were a heterogeneous mixture of artisans, small traders, failed artists, speculators and simple 'get-rich-quick' merchants, eager to profit from a new fashion. The technique was learned quickly, usually with no scientific understanding of the processes or equipment, and there was little concession to artistic taste. If the results were not too good, the daguerreotypist could always move on to the next town or village and start again. There were exceptions of course, especially in the major cities. Antoine Claudet became one of the most fashionable daguerreotypists and his fame was well earned, for he was a sensitive artist and a scientist of sufficient stature to be elected a Fellow of the Royal Society in 1853. Later, an increasing number of photographers were to rival Claudet's work, but there were always many operators whose sole object was to make money as quickly as possible. The cost of a licence and materials deterred amateurs from taking up the daguerreotype process in large numbers and in Britain it remained almost exclusively an art practised by professional portrait photographers.

In contrast, Talbot's calotype process (fig 6) was favoured by amateurs. The materials were comparatively cheap – good quality writing paper and a limited range of chemicals – and a licence for amateurs was available at minimal cost. The process was portable in comparison to the daguerreotype process and therefore more convenient for travellers. Its disadvantages, the coarser images and slightly longer exposure times, were no great drawback to the gentlemen artists and scientists who practised the art and found many static subjects to record. It had one great advantage that appealed to amateurs and professionals alike – copies could be easily duplicated in unlimited numbers. A surprising number of the people who used the paper process were relations, friends or acquaintances of Talbot's. His cousins in South Wales, Christopher (Kit) Talbot, Emma (née Talbot) and her husband John Dillwyn Llewelyn, were particularly enthusiastic exponents. Calvert Jones, their neighbour and friend, had retained his keen interest in photography partly through them, though he had heard of the calotype process directly from its inventor. Despite

CLAUDET'S

**DAGUERREOTYPE AND TALBOTYPE PORTRAIT**

ESTABLISHMENT,

**ROYAL ADELAIDE GALLERY,**

WITH GRATUITOUS PRIVATE ENTRANCE BY

**No. 18. KING WILLIAM STREET, STRAND,**

CORNER OF ADELAIDE STREET.

**Prices.**

DAGUERREOTYPE.

| | £ | s. | d. |
|---|---|---|---|
| Portrait on small Plate, including neat Morocco Case ........................ | 1 | 1 | 0 |
| Ditto on Plate, (without Case) 3-¼in. by 2¾ | 1 | 1 | 0 |
| Ditto ditto ........ 4 „ 3 | 1 | 11 | 6 |
| Ditto ditto ........ 5 „ 4 | 2 | 2 | 0 |
| Ditto ditto ........ 8½ „ 6½ | 5 | 5 | 0 |

Duplicates, half-price.

TALBOTYPE.

| | £ | s. | d. |
|---|---|---|---|
| Portrait on Sheet of Paper, 5-in. by 4 .. | 0 | 10 | 6 |
| Subsequent Copies, each ............ | 0 | 5 | 0 |
| Portrait on Sheet of Paper, 7 „ 5 .. | 1 | 1 | 0 |
| Subsequent Copies, each ............ | 0 | 7 | 6 |
| Portrait on Sheet of Paper, 9 „ 7 .. | 2 | 2 | 0 |
| Subsequent Copies, each ............ | 0 | 10 | 6 |

**OPEN EVERY DAY FROM TEN UNTIL DUSK.**

Figure 5 Advertisement for Claudet's photographic studio, c1845. Science Museum, London.

persistent efforts, Jones had never been able to produce good photogenic drawings, though he was much more successful with daguerreotypes. As he was keen to use a camera on his foreign travels and could appreciate that the copperplates essential to the daguerreotype process would be a weighty burden, Jones now renewed his attempts to master photography on paper. Unfortunately he again experienced failure, partly because Talbot's process was still in need of refinement. The development of calotype photography in Britain was to continue to revolve around its inventor.

In a sense this was unfortunate, as Talbot, a brilliant and far-sighted inventor, was no businessman and was temperamentally ill-equipped to exploit his invention commercially. He was certainly not averse to making money, but his many other interests prevented him from concentrating on this end exclusively, even though many around him thought he should. The astonishing success of the daguerreotype portrait studios led Talbot to hope that calotype portraits would prove to be equally popular with the public. In August 1841 he licensed a miniature-painter, Henry Collen, who opened the first professional calotype portrait studio in Somerset Street, London. Collen's portraits were received with interest by the press but failed to capture public imagination. Collen does not appear to have been a particularly skilful operator and he experienced a series of technical problems. He also showed no more business sense than Talbot and the venture failed within a year. Perhaps realising that marketing was a problem, Talbot approached Antoine Claudet with the offer of a licence. Claudet was anxious to ensure that he secured exclusive rights for the calotype in London while he perfected the technique and was in no hurry to conclude an agreement. Talbot and Claudet spent eighteen months haggling over terms and it was the summer of 1844 before agreement was reached. Claudet worked hard to make a success of calotype portraiture, but even with his experience and

Figure 6 Calotype portrait by Talbot of his daughter, Matilda (Tilly), 17 August 1843. Fox Talbot Collection, Science Museum, London.

reputation achieved little commercial success. The public were completely seduced by the exquisite detail of the daguerreotype and showed limited interest in calotype portraits. Claudet also experienced some of the technical problems that had plagued Collen and he was eventually forced to abandon commercial calotype portraiture. Despite this unhappy experience Claudet remained convinced that there was a long-term future for the calotype process. Perhaps the most important consequence of the enterprise was the firm friendship he formed with Talbot.

While he had been bogged down in negotiations with Claudet, Talbot had considered other ways of exploiting his invention. In 1843 he began planning a book of calotypes and in the next year set up a calotype printing establishment in Reading (fig 7), which was approximately halfway between his Lacock home and London. It was here that the prints were produced for *The Pencil of Nature*, the world's first commercial photographically-illustrated book. This seminal publication was issued in six parts between June 1844 and April 1846. It included a historical account of Talbot's invention of photography and twenty-four calotypes with an accompanying commentary. The choice of calotypes and the notes are revealing. Not a single portrait was included, but the work shows clearly that Talbot had a far more perceptive view of the future of photography than most of his contemporaries, and he anticipated much that is common practice today. Calotypes for other books were also produced at the Reading establishment. *Sun Pictures in Scotland*, a collection of scenes inspired by the writings of Sir Walter Scott, was published in 1845, and *The Talbotype Applied to Hieroglyphics* in 1846. In 1847, calotype copies of works of art were produced for twenty-five copies of Sir William Stirling's *Annals of the Artists of Spain*.

Talbot's Reading establishment was the first business formed to mass-produce photographs. As it was a completely novel venture there was, of course, no possibility of using

Figure 7 Talbot's calotype printing establishment at Reading, c1845. Fox Talbot Collection, Science Museum, London.

experienced staff. The establishment was placed under the direction of Talbot's one-time valet, Nicholaas Henneman, who recruited local assistants. The Harrison brothers were handymen who assisted with the printing while Henderson, an apprentice from the local stationers, looked after mundane clerical duties. They were later joined by Thomas Malone, a chemist's young assistant. Talbot also appointed an educated man, B Cowderoy, to deal with more complex correspondence. Vast numbers of prints were made at Reading, and a good proportion were sold individually at stationers and bookshops in Reading itself, and also in London, Oxford and other towns.[12] At first, most were made from Talbot's own negatives or from negatives made by Henneman and his assistants at Reading. Talbot was always keen to broaden the scope of his subjects, however, and he now began to look towards some of his associates to provide suitable material.

It was while Talbot was engrossed in the affairs of the Reading establishment that he began to renew his friendship with Calvert Jones. They had kept in touch since 1839 but it was not until 1845 that the relationship began to blossom. Jones had been frustrated by his inability to achieve consistent results with the calotype process, and in July 1845 he wrote to express his delight at the prospect of direct tuition from Talbot: 'I am particularly obliged by your kind remembrance of me with respect to your photographic tour; nothing can interest me more than this opportunity of seeing the process in field operation under your direction'.[13] Jones's tuition turned out to be a public demonstration, for when later that month Talbot wrote home of views he, Jones and Henneman had taken in York, he claimed 'crowds of admiring spectators surrounded the camera wherever we planted it'.[14]

Jones, perhaps more confident of his skills, then embarked on a short expedition of his own. On 23 September 1845 he wrote to Talbot: 'I send you the first fruits of my essays which I hope you will consider satisfactory. We have been at Hampton Court for a couple of days where they were done . . . I have made no failures except with one very bad sheet of paper which yielded a dark crop of carbonaceous looking stains'.[15] It is possible that the Hampton Court trip was an exercise to confirm that Jones's skills were adequate for a much more ambitious expedition. The closer contact with Talbot had completely confirmed Jones's devotion to the calotype cause, for earlier that same month he had written 'My zeal in the cause of your beautiful art would lead me to any places however distant in order that it might be promulgated, as I think it a shame on our country that it is not more known and appreciated'.[16] His zeal, in fact, led him to plan an extensive photographic tour of the Mediterranean (see pages 26–27 for another account of this tour). The tour was to be made with his friend (and Talbot's cousin) Kit Talbot, and Kit's sick wife, Lady Charlotte. All the paper for the photography was to be prepared at the Reading establishment where it was also planned to print the negatives. Talbot had wanted to market foreign views, which he hoped very much would have great public appeal. The primary purpose of the Mediterranean expedition was to improve Charlotte's health, but Talbot would have seen this as an opportunity to acquire foreign material and Jones was still enthusiastic about the prospect of taking a camera abroad.

Travelling through France, the party arrived in Malta towards the end of November 1845. Jones had planned his trip carefully, but he had few precedents to guide him and it would have been a miracle if the trip had gone smoothly. We live in an age where film can be purchased in the smallest communities almost anywhere in the world, and where it can be exposed, processed, finished and photographs collected all in a matter of hours. It is therefore difficult for us to fully appreciate Jones's problems. As well as the technical difficulties of performing a series of delicate chemical and optical manipulations in unfamiliar environmental conditions, Jones also suffered from irregular supplies and erratic communications. In the mid-19th century, Malta was a very long way away from the essential supplies and expertise of the Reading establishment. In his earliest letter from Malta, Jones made the first of many requests to Talbot for more iodised paper. He also experienced a problem familiar to modern travellers – he had arrived at his destination but parts of his luggage had not. 'I was much disappointed at finding that my box containing my chemicals and paper had not come, nor will it arrive before the 30th.'[17]

On 18 January 1846, he wrote to Talbot again about paper supplies: 'I write to say that the paper which you were so kind as to promise that you wd desire Henneman to send by the Achilles which left England on the 9th has not arrived. I am awre that the Peninsular and Orient Co (having no competitors) are most uncertain and capricious in transmitting parcels & have no doubt that the paper is lying at their office awaiting their good pleasure of dispatch'.[18] He urged Talbot to berate the company on his behalf but to little effect,for he wrote yet again in February that he was reduced to a mere '14 sheets'.[19] The paper finally arrived in March but there were other problems. The persistent seasonal winds made it almost impossible for him to photograph vegetation, 'especially Palm Trees',[20] which were in perpetual motion. Calotype exposure-times remained rather long, even in sunlight which, as Jones noted, 'is more energetic than in England'. Using a large camera on a bright day he found that about three minutes was required. Even using a smaller '1/4 sized camera' about twenty seconds was necessary.[21] Jones was also concerned that his negatives may not have kept in field conditions, and he accordingly made arrangements to send them back to the Reading establishment for printing. He wrote to Talbot: 'Captain Walters of the Warspite has kindly offered to take anything for us to England o I shall send my negatives for fear they might darken'. Despite all his problems Jones remained irrepressibly enthusiastic about the results of his work and was now looking forward to some financial reward for his efforts. His letter continued, 'I am sure that they wd sell extremely well here, as Malta has become a vast recipient of tourist and travellers, who wd all like memorials . . . If this hint enables you to realise an enormous sum, I hope you will give me a share'.[22]

The Malta party had been joined by another friend of Talbot's, the Reverend George Bridges. As well as taking more views, Jones spent some time instructing Bridges in the calotype process. The party was then tragically disrupted by the sudden death of Lady Charlotte. After making arrangements to send her body back to Wales, Jones and Kit Talbot continued on a modified form of the expedition. They moved on to Naples from where Jones wrote to Talbot on 29 April 1846, yet again expressing his worries about low stocks of paper. He was as enthusiastic as ever about his subjects but had again experienced exposure problems. Because he had 'spoilt' several views he noted 'I intend henceforth leaving all my views a much longer time in the camera'.[23] On 11 May he was in Rome and a new problem of technical supplies had arisen. 'I am extremely annoyed at having used all of a small bottle of gallic acid which I brought from England and cannot procure again in Italy. I got some Tannic acid at Naples and have done a few impressions but it gives very red results.'[24] Jones's Italian tour was terminated that month owing to a family illness and by early June he had returned to Britain. The total number of negatives he had made throughout the tour is uncertain, but it must have amounted to several hundred.

Back in England Jones found himself in unexpected financial difficulties and, anxious to sell his negatives to Talbot, he began to take a close interest in the Reading establishment. On 14 June 1846, he wrote to Talbot lamenting the 'discouraging' prospects for photography: 'The apathy of the British public about it is quite inexplicable but I cannot help thinking that your agents in London cannot be very active'.[25] Much to Jones's dismay Talbot now showed some reluctance to buy his negatives, claiming that his own financial situation was also a worry. A clue to Talbot's lukewarm response may also be found in a letter from Kit Talbot, who wrote from Naples of Jones's calotype activities. 'As for Jones, he has thought of nothing else since he left England, and I fear you may have a surfeit of Malta.'[26] Talbot did agree to print some of the negatives at the Reading establishment, an offer which Jones gratefully accepted, but no firm agreement was made in the short term because in December 1846 Jones was shown as owing the Reading establishment '£5.19.6d'.[27] It was only later that Jones became a major supplier of negatives to Talbot. Despite these problems, he applied his mind, with Talbot, to marketing calotypes. He investigated the advantages of coating prints with varnish, probably in an attempt to combat the recurring problem of fading, and tentatively explored the techniques of retouching and hand colouring, although both he and Talbot had reservations about the practice. Jones was later to produce a number of delicate hand-coloured prints. During December 1846 he visited the Reading establishment and gave Talbot a glowing written report on Mr Harrison and Mr Henneman, but was distinctly unflattering about Mr Cowderoy.[28]

But by 1846 the days of the Reading establishment were numbered. It was never profitable and Talbot certainly lost several thousand pounds on the venture. As Claudet's London licence had by then expired, Talbot determined to take his process to Britain's capital city, and asked Jones to manage the project. Although he had been enthusiastic about the prospects of a London studio, it was now Jones's turn to refuse Talbot. Talbot then turned to Henneman and Malone, and in 1847 they set up at 122 Regent Street. Although the business was intended primarily to be a portrait studio, Talbot had a variety of other ideas, including further issues of *The Pencil of Nature*, the sale of prints, paper, chemicals and so on, and offering instruction on his process. The project seemed to be making a sound start when Talbot appears suddenly to have tired of being a businessman. He began negotiations with Henneman and Malone which concluded in an agreement making them a virtual gift of the Regent Street studio. In theory, all formal responsibility for the business then passed from Talbot. In practice, both he and Jones freely offered advice and encouragement for some years to come. It is ironic that the Regent Street studio went on to be the only commercial calotype establishment with which Talbot was connected that enjoyed any success, and even that success was qualified and temporary. The studio survived, and at times almost thrived, for some four or five years. It then began to lose money, despite yet more support from Talbot. It finally closed in 1856.

Many hundreds of prints made from negatives by Talbot and Jones were sold by the Reading establishment and, later, the Regent Street studio. During a period when photography was popularly associated with the narrow field of daguerreotype portraits, the prints served to demonstrate the enormous potential of the new art to a small but influential section of the public. By this public they were generally judged to be an artistic success, yet calotype photography failed to earn for Talbot and Jones any significant financial reward. The only other major calotype operation during photography's first decade was based in Scotland. Between 1843 and 1848 the celebrated partnership of David Octavius Hill and Robert Adamson produced over 3000 negatives in their Edinburgh studio. They won critical acclaim in Scotland and their fame extended to England. Yet it is clear that they never came near to covering their expenses and their operation was also a commercial failure.

Why did commercial calotype photography fail? Perhaps it was because its practitioners lacked business acumen. Perhaps it was because there was always an uncertainty about its operation and a risk that the prints might fade. Perhaps it was merely fickle fashion. Final failure was due to technological change. In 1851 a new negative process was introduced. Using glass negatives, it allowed the production of an unlimited number of prints with a detail that surpassed the calotype. Within a few years the two pioneer processes, after a decade of preeminence, were both displaced from favour. The daguerreotype process, an overwhelming economic success, vanished for ever. Negative-positive photography, a financial failure, was transformed and lives on to the present day. Several thousands of those early images have also survived: technically and aesthetically they constitute a remarkable record of photography's first decade.

Figure 8 Lace, by Talbot, c1839. Fox Talbot Collection, Science Museum, London.

## NOTES

1 Fox Talbot Museum ms, uncatalogued letter: John R Traherne to Talbot, 8 March 1839.

2 W H Fox Talbot, *The Pencil of Nature*, 1844–6.

3 H J P Arnold, *William Henry Fox Talbot, Pioneer of Photography and Man of Science*, 1977, p 108.

4 *Gazette de France*, 6 January 1839. Quoted by H & A Gernsheim, *L.J.M. Daguerre*, 1968.

5 W H Fox Talbot, 'Some Account of the Art of Photogenic Drawing', *Philosophical Magazine*, XIV, 1839, pp 196–208.

6 Fox Talbot Museum ms LA 39–6, letter: Lady Elizabeth Feilding to Talbot, 3 (?) February 1839.

7 Fox Talbot Museum ms LA 39–4, letter: Lady Elizabeth Feilding to Talbot, (?) February 1839.

8 Fox Talbot Museum ms LA 39–8, letter: Talbot to Lady Elizabeth Feilding, 5 February 1839.

9 Robert Hunt, *A Popular Treatise on the Art of Photography*, Introduction, 1841.

10 Science Museum, Fox Talbot Collection ms 3 (10), letter: J B Biot to Talbot, 10 November 1839.

11 According to Gernsheim, *op cit*, p 155.

12 See V F Snow and D B Thomas, 'The Talbotype establishment at Reading', *Photographic Journal*, February 1966, pp 56–67.

13 Fox Talbot Museum ms LA 45–103, letter: Calvert Jones to Talbot, 19 July 1845.

14 Quoted by Arnold, *op cit*, p 145.

15 Fox Talbot Museum ms LA 45–131, letter: Calvert Jones to Talbot, 23 September 1845.

16 Fox Talbot Museum ms LA 45–123, letter: Calvert Jones to Talbot, 4 September 1845.

17 Fox Talbot Museum ms LA 45–151, letter: Calvert Jones to Talbot, 24 November 1845.

18 Fox Talbot Museum ms LA 46–15, letter: Calvert Jones to Talbot, 18 January 1846.

19 Fox Talbot Museum ms LA 46–26; letter: Calvert Jones to Talbot, 13 February 1846.

20 Fox Talbot Museum ms LA 46–40, letter: Calvert Jones to Talbot, 15 March 1846.

21 Fox Talbot Museum ms LA 46–15, *op cit* (note 18).

22 Fox Talbot Museum ms LA 46–26, *op cit* (note 19).

23 Fox Talbot Museum ms LA 46–54, letter: Calvert Jones to Talbot, 29 April 1846.

24 Fox Talbot Museum ms LA 46–58, letter: Calvert Jones to Talbot, 11 May 1846.

25 Fox Talbot Museum ms LA 46–78, letter: Calvert Jones to Talbot, 14 June 1846.

26 Fox Talbot Museum ms LA 46–56, letter: C R M Talbot to Talbot, 30 May 1846.

27 Fox Talbot Museum ms LA 46–128, list: 'Monies owing to the Talbotype Establishment', December 1846.

28 Fox Talbot Museum ms LA 46–132, letter: Calvert Jones to Talbot, 4 December 1846.

# CALVERT RICHARD JONES

The social sphere into which the third Calvert Richard Jones was born in 1802 allowed him to follow a life of eclecticism. He was a talented dilettante watercolourist, an avid traveller, and a persevering student in mastering the technique of the calotype. He was one of the few gifted amateurs to apply the principles of artistic composition during the formative two decades of photography. His patrimony afforded him a position among the landed gentry of Swansea, South Wales, and his lineage can be traced through the ownership of several estates there: the Plas, Veranda, and Heathfield Lodge.

Jones's ancestry can be traced back to 1383, when John de Horton commenced building the Plas, a manor house in Swansea. It was completed by his descendant, Captain Sir Mathew Cradock, who died there in 1521. His daughter Margaret married Richard Herbert, and their son, George, who was knighted about 1543, lived in the Plas until his death in 1570. The Plas remained in the Herbert family until 1746, when it passed through the maternal heirs to Calvert Richard Jones of Gloucester, who had married Elizabeth Allen, sister of Elizabeth Parker Herbert.

Calvert and Elizabeth Jones had five children: Calvert R Jones; George, who became a captain in the Royal Navy; and Elizabeth, Sarah and Lucy, all spinsters. In 1801, the second Calvert Jones married Prudence Sproule. They lived at Veranda, where their first son, Calvert Richard Jones, was born. The other children of Calvert and Prudence were Herbert George Jones, sergeant at law and metropolitan judge of county courts; Henry Wyndam Jones, Rector of Loughor; and two daughters, Prudence Elizabeth Frances and Georgiana Cecilia. Unlike his father, who had had a dispute with the locals over the Plas boundary and thereafter kept to himself, the second Calvert Jones was active in public life. He was to receive many appointments and honours because of his contribution to civic affairs. He was elected a burgess of the Corporation of Swansea, and became a trustee of the harbour and an alderman. In 1828 he gave the city a valuable gift of property known as 'Ropewalk Field', so that a new market-place could be built. It was opened in 1830. In 1813 Jones purchased

Heathfield Lodge, and lived there with Prudence until his death in 1847. Veranda was then occupied by Prudence's relatives – a son by her first marriage, Rawleigh Addenbrooke Mansel, and the Ireland Joneses, of whom their nephew, Calvert Richard Jones, later wrote: 'Colonel Jones and herself always behaved as parents to us'.[1]

Calvert Richard Jones was born on 4 December 1802. He was educated at Oriel College, Oxford, where he obtained a first class degree in mathematics in 1823. He became a close friend of Christopher Rice Mansel Talbot (1803–90), cousin of William Henry Fox Talbot (1800–77), who looked after Christopher (Kit) during his earlier schooling.

> *In 1820 Kit went to Oriel College, Oxford where he read Mathematics. Whilst at Oxford he seems to have reformed, taking a greater interest in his studies and becoming greatly interested in all scientific matters. One of his contemporaries at Oxford became a close personal friend; this was the Rev. Calvert Richard Jones (1802–1877), a member of a wealthy Swansea family with whom he shared a common interest in the arts, travel, science and mathematics.*[2]

Kit graduated in 1824, attained his majority, and inherited his vast wealth. 'Wielding almost feudal powers, this heir to the ancient and proud lineage of the Mansel Talbot families was patron of six livings.'[3] In contrast, Jones lived in relative penury until 1847, when his inheritance gave him financial independence. Late in 1824 Kit took Jones and several companions on the first of many tours to the Mediterranean to purchase works of art. Their continuing close companionship was noted by Fox Talbot in a letter to his mother in August 1830 from the Isle of Wight, where he was on holiday. 'Kit is here in the Galatea [one of his many yachts] with his usual satellite, Calvert Jones.'[4]

In 1829 Jones entered holy orders and accepted the living of Loughor in a small town near Penllergaer, on a bluff overlooking the River Loughor. He was also lay Rector of St Mary's of Swansea, but only because of his family's ownership of the Cradock Chapel. He abandoned his profession about the time of his first marriage, but conducted the wedding of his brother, Herbert George, to Maria Leeds in 1830, and that of Kit Talbot to Lady Charlotte Butler, daughter of the Earl of Glengall, at Cahir House, County

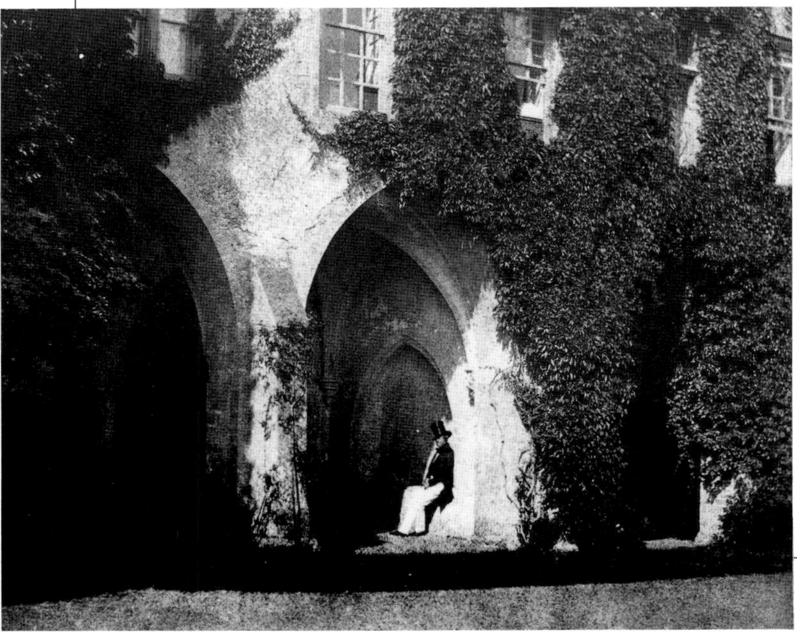

Figure 9 Calvert Jones in the vestry, Lacock Abbey, c1844. Science Museum, London.

Tipperary, Ireland in 1835 – an important social occasion. His other brother, Henry Wyndham Jones, who became Rector of Loughor after Calvert abandoned it, performed the ceremony for Calvert's first marriage on 25 July 1837 at Ystradgynlais, a small community about twenty miles from Swansea. Anne Harriet, eldest daughter of Howell Jones Williams of Coity Mawr, Brecon, was his bride, and their only child was Christina Henrietta Victoria Games. They established a household in 1853 at 9 Rue de Londres in Brussels, where Anne Harriet later died on 2 January 1856. Jones's second marriage was to Portia Jane, only daughter of James Smith of Dover. The wedding took place at St James Church, Dover, on 20 May 1858, and Jones's obituary states that they had two daughters, but their names are not known (see Appendix A2).

When he became owner of Heathfield after his father's death in 1847, Jones had firm opinions on how Swansea should develop. This was exemplified by his 'opposition to the Corporation's efforts to have the Music Hall (later the Albert Hall) built on the former slaughterhouse site at the junction of Tontine Street and Orchard Street. He refused to meet a deputation, "What can there be to discuss?" So it was built, in De-la-Beche Street. At that time there could have been no better site, and it was one freely given by himself out of his Heathfield estate'.[5] He named Christina Street after his daughter, Mansel Street after his half-brother, Portia Terrace after his second wife, Veranda Street after the house in which he had been born, and Calvert Terrace after his father. Calvert Street had already been named after his grandfather.

He had a bitter imbroglio with the Reverend Edward Burnard Squire, of St Mary's Church, Swansea, who acted unilaterally in the affairs of the church. Jones, Impropriator of St Mary's, considered that he should be consulted about the removal of the church galleries and the placing of memorial inscriptions. We can only assume that the Reverend Squire was intractable, and that finally Jones grumbled off in self-imposed exile to Lansdown Crescent, Bath, where he lived the rest of his life, interspersed with numerous excursions to the

Figure 10 Inscribed 'Cahir' and dated 'Octr 24. 1835'. Pen and watercolours. Martyn Gregory Gallery, London.

Continent. After his death at Lansdown Crescent on 7 November 1877, his body was interred at St Mary's, despite the hostility that still existed. He still held title to the Cradock Chapel and could not be denied burial with his Herbert ancestors.

Christina died before her father, on 29 June 1877. In 1859 she had married Alfred Grey, the ninth son of the Hon Edward Grey, Bishop of Hereford. They had six children, the eldest of whom was Colonel Sir Raleigh Grey of the 6th Dragoons. He inherited the Swansea and Porthcawl properties, and in 1902 held the first of many auctions which disposed of the whole estate. 'The late Ernest Holtham Leeder, who knew Raleigh Grey, described him as an absentee landlord who wanted to cash in'.[6]

## *Jones as an artist*

The enormous estate auction of 1902 and the extensive exhibition, at around the same time, of the art of three generations of the Harris family, stimulated several publications reflecting on the time of Jones and his association with the elder James Harris. An anonymous manuscript, 'Old Swansea: Some Very Interesting Reminiscences', refers to Jones's father and the art of Jones himself:

> *At Heathfield lived Sir Gabriel Powell, not a baronet, but a simple K.B., or Knight Bachelor. Subsequently came Mr. Calvert Jones, whose public spirit and interest in the affairs of the town took substantial form when he presented to the burgesses, as a free gift, that extensive and valuable tract of ground between Oxford and Orange Streets, for the purpose of a market, and where now stands a market place, which, so far as I know, is second to none in the country.*
>
> *This Mr. Calvert Jones (of Heathfield) had several sons, the eldest, I think, was the Revd. Calvert Jones, who I believe, never donned a surplice, but devoted himself very much to a splendid white Pomeranian dog he had, and to oil painting, his subjects being remarkable, for they were almost invariably shipping, not ships afloat, but lying high and dry in harbour or on the beach. Many were taken inside the piers and I have watched the artist sitting there, opposite his easel, in dangerous proximity to the mud. They always seemed to be what an artist might call conventional drawings, and I do not suppose the waterline of*

*the ship or any part of the hull, or the perspective would be out of drawing, even if judged by the rules of Euclid. They were highly proper, highly coloured and attractive to the eye. There must be many of them in or about Swansea even now. Mr. Jones was a long while a great personal friend of the late Mr. Talbot [Kit].*[7]

The *South Walian* noted 'The Harris collection of paintings in connection with the annual exhibition of the Swansea Art Society and the Royal Institution of South Wales during the first two weeks of December, 1902 created a good deal of interest in Swansea and district'. The article was largely devoted to the Harrises, but also corroborates the relationship between Jones, Harris and Chambers: 'About the time mentioned Mr. Calvert Jones introduced him [Harris] to George Chambers, the great marine painter (some of whose battle scenes are to be seen hanging in Greenwich Hospital), and he became his pupil in London and worked in his studio for some time'.[8]

It is not known where Jones trained as an artist, but 'Tradition has it that Samuel Prout and John Whichelo gave him instruction. His early work shows simple pencil drawings [fig 11], and watercolour is used in washes. Later he worked on tinted paper, in pencil, applying opaque white to the highlights and coloured washes.'[9] Samuel Prout is known for his watercolours of picturesque, romantic landscapes of England, Wales and the Continent. His subtle use of earth colours contrasting with the cold colours of sea and sky, together with his careful attention to the rules of perspective, had considerable influence on his students and later imitators. John Whichelo, noted principally for his marine watercolours, practised in London and became marine painter to the Prince Regent. Both Prout and Whichelo were members of the Old Water-Colour Society.

Jones's letter to Fox Talbot, on 14 June 1846, offers evidence that he was acquainted with members of the Old Water-Colour Society: 'Your enclosure of a Prospectus has just arrived, I think it is very well drawn up, and if well acted upon must I should think answer

Figure 11 Inscribed 'Calstock of Swansea'. National Library of Wales, Aberystwyth.

. . . If you will send me a few of those Prospectuses, I think I could send them with advantage to Harding and other persons'.[10] It is possible that the Harding mentioned is James Duffield Harding, who was educated in art by his father John, then by Samuel Prout, and later by Charles Pye, the engraver. Harding was a teacher throughout his life, with John Ruskin being his most notable student. Harding and Chambers were also members of the Old Water-Colour Society, and it was probably the same Harding who accompanied Jones at the reading of his paper to the Photographic Society of London in 1853. It is possible, then, that Prout, Whichelo, Harding and Chambers had some formative influence on Jones's abilities as an artist.

Jones preferred maritime subjects but also drew environmental portraits and architectural backgrounds. His larger watercolours are mostly ships afloat, in the tradition of the ship portrait of the eighteenth century, and have considerable action in them, like the paintings of the elder James Harris. Jones's smaller sketchbook watercolours are closer in subject-matter and style to the Norwich School, with quiet studies of beached boats and grounded hulls in harbours and tidal estuaries. His technique in either format is very controlled, like that of the draughtsman or illustrator, rather than having the painterly quality of the traditional watercolourist.

When Jones began to use the camera he was faced with a new set of compositional problems, such as the open composition and the arbitrary limitation of the camera frame. There were no teachers and no models to emulate. This pioneering exploration must have produced great excitement in Jones and his contemporaries.

## *Jones as a photographer*

Jones's attraction to photogenic drawing and to the calotype was not a sudden and overwhelming frisson. He was, however, intrigued with Talbot's invention of photogenic drawing, as is evidenced in the letter which Talbot's cousin, Charlotte Traherne, wrote in 1839, when the knowledge of the process had arrived in Wales:

*Penllergaer*
*Feb. 28th*

*My Dear Henry,*

*I am charmed with the piece of lace [photogenic image] you sent, it is much too pretty for you to have it again. John Llewelyn has been making some paper according to your process and they are all busy trying little scraps of lace and ribbon. One succeeded very well this morning before breakfast but the day is clouding over. Mr Calvert Jones is quite wild about it and I dare say by this time is making experiments in Swansea for himself. John Llewelyn's paper turns out browner than your piece and not so dark. We put a piece in the camera obscura but got only a faint outline or rather shadowing of the laces – but the sun was not strong or steady.*[11]

Fascinated as Jones was with the phenomenon of an object making its own image on a piece of paper through the action of light, when news of the daguerreotype process was disseminated he was quick to respond. Between 1840 and 1841 he learned the technique and achieved success, as is evidenced by the daguerreotype of Margam Castle (fig 12, CM13 in catalogue). On the blue paper backing of the passepartout is Jones's inscription and signature: 'March 9t 1841 9h. 30m. A.M./ In the Camera 26 min. Sun clear throughout./ Mercury 7 min. rising 9 falling./ Calvert R. Jones'.

Talbot's calotype process was patented in February 1841. In May 1841 Jones, planning a trip to Italy and not wanting to carry heavy daguerreotype plates, wrote to Talbot, wanting details of how to make calotypes. Talbot obliged, for Jones responded:

Figure 12 Daguerreotype of Margam Castle (cat. no. CM13). National Library of Wales, Aberystwyth.

*Heathfield. June 4th 1841*

*My dear Sir,*

*I return you many, many thanks for your prompt kindness in sending me the note to M. Biot, and for the beautiful Calotypes, with which I was really delighted. The marble head is equal to one of M. Angelo's drawings, and the small bit of Lacock wonderfully pictorial and strong, also the large one of the back yard sunny in the extreme, the foliage I think brighter than any one on silver that I have seen.*

*These specimens have charmed me so much that I am very anxious to learn the method before we go. You can best tell me whether any oral instruction is very necessary (in many such cases it is) if it should be so I would take advantage of your kind offer of speaking to me on the subject.*

*We propose leaving here the 19th and to go from Southampton to Havre, but as Mrs. Jones wishes to stay 2 days at Clifton I might run up to London if you should be there on the 20 and 21st should it be desirable to do so.*

*I should imagine that a stock of best English paper would be at all events a sine qua non; my only apology for intruding on your valuable time is the great interest I take in the subject and the just appreciation of very high services unrivalled in my opinion to the cause of art.*[12]

The years 1841 to 1845 were for Jones a time of minimum success with the calotype. The images from his Italian excursion were a failure. He persevered, but the results were erratic and unpredictable. The paper and not the manipulation of the chemicals appeared to be the problem, and he was frustrated at not being able to get the results that Talbot demonstrated. Fine writing-paper was all that Talbot specified. Other calotypists must have suffered similar disappointments, as W H Thornthwaite insinuated in an 1843 pamphlet:

*The first difficulty the Calotype has to contend with, is to obtain a paper of sufficient fine and even texture, and free from all foreign matter in its substance, which would cause blemishes in the picture. – The best kind is that called blue wove, or bank post, and each sheet, preparatory to its being used, should be carefully examined before a strong light, and those sheets rejected in which any spots or uneven texture is observed.*[13]

These generic names of paper may be descriptions of that produced by J Whatman, which Talbot used. In any event, Jones discovered Whatman's Turkey Mill quite independently, and described his failures and discoveries to Talbot:

*Veranda, Swansea*
*Feb. 15 1845*

*My dear Sir,*

*Accept my best thanks for your kind present of the Pencil of Nature which I am anxiously expecting.*

*I have made some attempts with the present increasing light to do a Talbotype worthy of sending you, but, though I succeed in Daguereotyping* [sic] *as well as any performer whose results I have seen, there is some little point wanting which has hitherto prevented me from doing the same in your beautiful branch of the Photographic art.*

*My Iodized paper is beautifully even and well coloured and after washing it with* A *and exposing in Camera, and then washing with* B *the image begins to come very well without any heat, but in general without a sufficient range (if I may so express it) in the gamut of Chiaroscuro: i.e. the whitest parts begin to discolour before the darkest have become black enough: also, sometimes I have had stains something like the discolouration of lichen on stone which seem to be rather on the back of the picture, and to be more visible after the washing with hot Hyposulphate* [sic] *of soda.*

*These stains however do not always occur, and my principal bar to good pictures has been the want of intensity above mentioned.*

*As far as making paper J.D. Llewelyn has succeeded better, but he yesterday told me, it is with some sold by Whatman for the especial purpose; he and I are going to try and do some Marine Talbotypes in the port of Swansea which we hope may perhaps be acceptable for the "Pencil of Nature" . . .*

*Lady C. Talbot wrote us word two days ago that you have made wonderful improvements; I am most anxious to hear what they are, and if they are not secrets, should be infinitely obliged if you would at your leisure let me hear of them, as I have no doubt they will much add to the certainty of the results which I hope soon to arrive at.*

*I have mislaid a positive picture which had wished to send you: it was thus produced, – happening to drop a little wax from a candle on a group which had come out very well after the gallic acid wash, I laid it face upwards on a table in the sun, and soon after, on taking it up I found a positive picture on the underside.*

*Among other improvements have you directed your attention to copying paper? Llewelyn is fond of preparing it with succinic acid, but I have not tried it.*[14]

Talbot indeed had his 'secrets', but it seems unlikely that he would have been circumspect about the kind of paper he used, in view of the many other pieces of information about the process which he shared. A more direct sharing occurred in July 1845, when Jones was invited to join Talbot and Nicholaas Henneman on a photographic excursion to York, bringing together their technical and artistic talents. Talbot wrote to his mother relating the experience:

*York Monday*
*28th July 1845*

*My Dear Mother*

*The Binder is binding three copies of No. 1 for you, there are no more plates left for I made a search the other day to see if there were any more. When Nicole [Henneman] returns to Reading I will desire him to print off more copies of the plates of No. 1.*

*Mr. Calvert Jones is just arrived to unite his photographic efforts with mine. He says he had a narrow escape just on arriving at his journey's end; the luggage on the roof of the railway carriage caught fire and immediately a gentleman exclaimed Oh! The gun-powder! for he had 4 pounds of powder in his portmanteau; fortunately they were near York and the train stopped before the fire had communicated to this fatal portmanteau.*[15]

On the 29th, Talbot wrote to his wife, Constance: 'Mr. Jones does not seem the worse for his fright for he got up extremely early this morning and took a long walk thro' the city, studying the points of view, before breakfast. We took 12 views of York today, most of them good – crowds of admiring spectators surrounded the camera wherever we planted it'.[16] It cannot be ascertained with any certainty which photographs made at York were from the hand of Talbot, Jones or Henneman, as they are all quite similar in distancing and angle of view. It may even be possible that Jones coached his mentor in camera placement. It can be observed from other examples of Jones's street views that he favoured a point of view more obliquely composed, producing an asymmetrical balance different from Talbot's usual symmetrical, frontal confrontation of the subject.

This singularly important cooperative event, 'to unite his photographic efforts with mine', seems to have established a firm relationship between the two men, encouraging Jones to continue as a more confident calotypist well beyond the experimental stage. One month following the York photographic efforts, Jones wrote to Talbot: 'I have been eagerly expecting the iodized paper which Henneman promised to furnish me with as I am most anxious to try my hand; and put it off till the receipt of this as I wish to begin with successful "coups" for encouragement; and to send you something new in the marine line for the "Pencil of Nature"'.[17]

Jones was intensely interested in the calotype achieving commercial success, and wanted to be directly involved in that success. With entrepreneurial enthusiasm, he wrote to Talbot from London:

*159 Regent Street*
*Monday, Oct. 5, 1845*

*My dear Sir,*

*I enclose a specimen of which one half is varnished, the rest only fixed, this being an indispensable part of the process which Mr. Winsor has been so good as to teach me; by diluting the varnish it may be made less shiny, though I do not know whether this is any advantage.*

*I mentioned to Mr. Winsor [of Winsor and Newton, Artists' Suppliers] what Mr. Brookes had proposed to you with respect to the sale of Talbotypes, and the introduction of them to the notice of the world, and he said that he thought there could be few houses less calculated for the purpose, this opinion he expressed without impugning the respectability of Mr. Brookes's house in the slightest degree, but merely conceived that commercially speaking, it was not in the most direct line for your purpose. He thought if Ackerman [print-sellers] could be induced to do the same thing it would for instance be much better as he conceived it was principally through artists buying Talbotypes as studies, and making them known as such to their employers and pupils that a really extensive sale of them could be established.*

*As therefore he has previously told me that his agents travelled not only to every town of any size in the United Kingdom but also to great numbers on the Continent, for the purpose of taking orders from artists and colour shops, it struck me that he might possibly be of more important use to you in this aspect than any one else, and I therefore asked his opinion on the subject.*

*He expressed great readiness to assist, and said he thought the best way would be to supply his travelling agents with a large number to distribute gratuitiously, and also prospectuses with regard to the sale of Talbotypes. I told him I would write to you, and feel gratified that I happened to think of what will perhaps be the best means of making the Talbotype known. I should recommend you to come to town the first convenient opportunity that you may confer with Mr. Winsor.*

*He was much pleased with the Lacock specimens, but thought the sawyers at the shed worth the whole system for the purpose to which he thinks they may be principally applied, viz for the use of artists, and justly thought that nature was inexhaustible in such materials, provided they were artistically chosen.*

*Everybody to whom I have shown the specimens you sent has been charmed with them. I think the entrance of the chapel the finest that has yet been done. Mr. Malone at Claudets told me that he had last week seen some very fine ones done by an amateur who adds some combination of sodium in preparing Iodized paper which increases the sensitivity.*

*I have instructed your cousin, who is much pleased with his success; I forgot to say that the not very splendid little specimen which Kit inserted in my last note was his first essay. He will be glad of some more Iodized paper than the 100 sheets. I shall also wish for some as soon as convenient, the Talbots think of going the end of the week, his paper must therefore be soon sent if he is to take it.*

*We have determined on staying till Wednesday, or perhaps till this day weeks, I may therefore perhaps hope to see you; if it should be inconvenient to you to visit London now, and you wish me to say anything to Mr. Winsor I shall be happy to do so.*[18]

All of this intense interest in marketing photographs may have been prompted by the anticipated voyage to Malta, which Jones was to make with Kit Talbot. (See pages 10–11 for another account of this expedition.) Kit usually took his winter holidays in Nice or Italy, but was advised by Lady Charlotte's physician to go to a more temperate climate. Lady Charlotte had been suffering with a serious respiratory ailment for several months. Departing for Malta were Jones, his wife Ann Harriet and daughter Christina (age 6); Lady Charlotte, Kit, his daughter Olivia (age 3); and perhaps the other young Talbot children, Theodore (age 6),

Emily (age 5), and Bertha (age 4). They arrived in November, and Jones wrote to Henry Talbot:

*Valetta, Dec. 1, 1845*

*My dear Sir,*

*I wrote in such haste last week, that I forgot to tell you that when at Paris, I went to see M. Bayard, who is succeeding very fairly in negative Photography, and also in the copies.* His system is of course a secret, but he told me it was much more simple and easy of manipulation than yours, this however is nothing to the purpose which I meant to tell you, and that is respecting his paper, which appears to come out very even and without spots; he was kind enough to give me a few sheets for you; I send these and hope they may answer, he also gave me the address of the manufacturer, which I have mislaid, but do not doubt that I shall find it.*

*At Lyons, Avignon, and Marseilles I saw some Photographs which the shopkeepers at the houses where they were exposed represented as being paper Dags, but which, from certain identical stains on different copies, I discovered to be a kind of Talbotype; they appeared to be quickly done, as several figures appeared.*

*They were done by an Italian named Lenchi, who is prepared to reveal his method whenever a certain number (how many I know not) of persons shall have agreed to give him 100 francs each. I did not see him, but all the Photographers I have met with are delighted with my paper specimens.*

*You need not be the least alarmed lest I should reveal any thing to these gentlemen.*

*I sincerely trust that the 1st Liverpool will bring me my Talbotype battery tomorrow as the subjects here are splendid.*

*The Talbots have not as yet been able to find a house. Lady C. remains I think much the same but enjoys the lovely climate in . . . boating etc.; the weather is as warm, and much more sunny than an English June.*[19]

This excursion marks the beginning of the most productive period in Jones's photographic career. For the four months Jones lived in Malta, he made calotypes of harbours and ships, portraits of visiting Greeks in costume, environmental studies and street views. Such a prolific output seems understandable, since there was little else to do while waiting for Lady Charlotte's health to improve. Although the weather was unstable, Jones continued to use the supply of iodized paper.

*Valetta, March 15, 1846*

*My dear Sir,*

*I have received through a merchant here my 100 sheets of Paper, and hasten to acknowledge them. I trust that you have ere this received my proofs. Since receiving my new paper I have gone to work again very successfully, but the weather has lately been not very propitious.*

*With respect to vegetation, great difficulty exists; as in this place a calm day appears to be an unknown thing, at least such has been the case for 4 months and it is therefore impossible to do any plants, especially Palm trees.*

*I am giving Mr. Bridges every instruction as you requested, tomorrow we go to St. Pauls bay, a highly interesting locale.*

*I trust to do a good deal now that I am supplied with "material".*

*I am sorry to say that our dear Invalid has become very weak, but trust it may yet please God to restore her.*

*With united kind regards, I am*[20]

The Rev George Wilson Bridges was introduced to Henry Talbot through an acquaintance with Talbot's half-sister, Lady Caroline. Bridges was an ardent traveller and author of *Annals of Jamaica*, 1827. Having seen the calotype, and eager to record his travels, he secured permission from Talbot to be instructed by Henneman. Jones also agreed to coach Bridges. The final reference in the letter indicates the continued deterioration of Lady Charlotte's health, and she died in Malta on 2 April 1846. Kit Talbot's yacht, the *Galatea*, anchored in Valetta harbour, took Lady Charlotte's body back to Port Talbot and then to Margam, where she was interred in the family vault. Kit could not return because Olivia was also ill, and could not make the voyage. She apparently soon recovered and they continued their excursion, to Sicily, Naples, Pompeii, Rome and Florence. The Joneses' tour was terminated in Rome by news of the imminent death of Colonel Jones of Veranda. Jones wrote to Talbot:

*Veranda. June 9, 1846*
*Swansea*

*My dear Sir,*

*During my stay of a few hours in London, I called in Sackville Street on Saturday last, and was much disappointed at not seeing you, as you are still in England.*

*The latter part of our journey from Italy was extremely hurried, from unavailing efforts to see our poor friend Colonel Jones alive.*

*If Henneman has made copies of all the negatives which I sent home, I shall be much obliged if you will order me copies of them all, being naturally very anxious to see them.*

*I have nearly 100 large, and about 20 small negatives, all highly interesting, done in Malta, Sicily, Naples (a series at Pompeii) Rome and Florence, most of them are wonderfully perfect and beautiful; and in all I have endeavoured to follow your advice in overdoing them, so that I doubt not they will come out extremely well.*

*I cannot help thinking that the whole series (including what I sent home from Malta) are worth something considerable, and as circumstances have arisen which will, I fear, cause extraneous claims on my present narrow means, I should be very glad to concert with you some plan, by which I could make the art I am so fond of, repay me the trouble it occasions, either by your giving me so much for negatives or by allowing me to sell a certain number of copies.*

*As for Malta, it will afford me unceasing market for views done there, from the everlasting succession of travellers and the continually shifting garrison and fleet. Rome also and Naples would afford a constant demand.*

*The best artists, to whom I have shown specimens, have been perfectly enchanted, especially with details and foregrounds and as nature is infinite, so is the supply which I could furnish: the great point being to select the proper subjects from a proper position.*

*I shall be extremely obliged if you will write me a few lines as soon as you can conveniently, since if I cannot make some arrangement with you concerning Photography, I shall be obliged to turn my thoughts to something else "My Poverty and not my will consents."*

*We have not heard from your Cousin since we left Rome, having been in constant motion, should you have any news of him, it will be most acceptable.*[21]

His letter of 13 July 1846 to Talbot expresses continued financial distress and a desperate need to market his images in one way or another:

*Veranda, July 13th 1846*

*My dear Sir,*

*I was very glad that my 2nd list of views pleased you, and will send some to Henneman to copy.*

*It would give me the greatest pleasure to connect myself with you in your Photographic enterprises, as I am so fond of the Art, and take the deepest interest in its success; if I could secure any certain emolument by it, as it is to that which I must for the present, look.*

*As for ourselves, we are content with the little we receive during my Father's life; but the provisions of Col. Jones's will have left my Aunt so badly provided for, that as she has always been accustomed to an excellent establishment, which was a home to us, I feel bound to endeavour to make her remaining days as comfortable as possible.*

*I do not know whether you have any interest, but if you or any other friends could assist me in procuring a Living, or any appointment which I am capable of holding I should be very glad to assist you to the utmost of my ability in the Photographic line.*

*Did you see the praise and admiration of your Art expressed in the Spring no. of the Quarterly? It is in the 1st Article "On German Art."*

*I think it would be much better if the description of the particular views were placed (even written in pencil) under each, in front.*[22]

Another way in which Jones attempted to make his images appeal to the public was to hand-colour them. Over a lightly printed image were brushed a combination of watercolour and opaque body-colour (gouache) pigments. Sometimes figures were introduced, as illustrated in Merchant Street, Valetta, with the Scots Guard and the townsfolk (H-C2 in the catalogue) and the Bay of Naples embellished with figures (H-C3 in the catalogue). A further artistic insinuation is Jones's painting in of the volcanic action of Vesuvius in the background of the House of Sallust (AP3 and H-C1 in the catalogue).

Figure 13 House of Sallust, Pompeii (cat. no. AP3). Science Museum, London.

Figure 14 House of Sallust, Pompeii (cat. no. HC1). David Alan Brown collection, Washington DC.

*Veranda, March 28 1847*

*Dear Sir,*

*I sent the P6 order to you, because I was not sure where to find Henneman.*

*My coloured specimens have gone to London to be mounted, after which I have desired that they should be sent to Mansfield Street.*

*The prices which I consider them well worth are £1 for large views, £2 for large double (views), 10s for the half size (of which numbers 26 and 28 are specimens) and 6s each for the quarter size. I could not possibly take less; especially for the first or original copies, as they require a great deal of trouble, and more than that, much artistical knowledge and tact.*

*I find that I can improve continually in the treatment of them, and think that they are capable and worthy of much art being expended on them, particularly if we could do them of a larger size.*

*Enclosed is a list, which had better be kept, and I hope that they will be carefully kept clean.*

*I have written to ask Henneman to have a few simple gold beadings with glass made to show them in, when he gets the size of the mounting boards and by that when they are shown they may have the glass over them, as the effect is much better.*

Figure 15 Inscribed 'No. 50 Street at Pompeii leading to the Forum' (cat. no. AP4, positive). Science Museum, London.

Figure 16 Street at Pompeii (cat. no. AP4, negative). Science Museum, London.

*I am sorry that you have not yet concluded with the Parish authorities and am extremely anxious to hear how you have got on with your accelerating process as I am very desirous of trying it: I shall begin some double and treble views as soon as the sun comes, which I daily hope.*[23]

Further innovative techniques, used partly out of artistic innovation and partly out of necessity, were those of inking in skies and filling in portions of lost images. Inking the sky opaque produced a clear sky, free from blemishes caused by the paper. Instructions on how to achieve the intended effect were given to the printer (AP4 in the catalogue). A final innovative technique was the creation of 'joiners' or 'double and treble views', as Jones calls them in his letter – joining two calotypes together and having them register as a complete, unbroken panorama (HS112 and HS113 in the catalogue). Jones illustrated his desire to increase the field of vision in one of his sketchbooks as well (fig 18). On 5 May 1853 he

Figure 17 Inscribed '42 Ste. Lucia joins 43 at . . . Naples' (cat. nos. HS112, HS113). Science Museum, London.

presented a paper, 'On a Binocular Camera', to the newly formed Photographic Society of London.[24] (See Appendix A3.) The device was not to produce a stereoscopic effect, but to increase the angle of view on an unjoined, single sheet of paper.

The letter of March 1847 was the last one in which Jones complained of poverty, for his father's 'will of 20 April 1841, with codicil of 1842, was proved in St. David's Registry 7 October 1847'.[25] His activities in 1853 are an indication of his newly acquired financial independence: he had his passport renewed for Nice in March, London in May, and Brussels in November. His letter of 26 May 1853, perhaps his last to Talbot, serves as an epilogue to his association with him by praising the Talbotype process, showing interest in Talbot's new experiments in photoglyphic engraving, and despairing of his own frustration with the quality of paper, which had plagued him throughout his photographic career.

*May 26, 1853*

*Dear Sir,*

*Accept my thanks for the beautiful impressions you were so good to send me, they appear to be as perfect as possible of their kind.*

*I do not know whether you have yet extended the method to views, but I trust soon to see it adapted to them as it would be a great desideratum.*

*I think you may have the satisfaction of knowing that your method of Photography (Talbotype proper) is superior practically to waxed paper, albumenised etc., etc., or any other that has yet been devised.*

Figure 18 'Bay of Naples'. National Library of Wales.

*The only bar (and I think it quite disgraceful to the manufacturer) is the next to impossibility of procuring good negative paper.*

*Yours most truly*

*Calvert R. Jones.*[26]

## NOTES

1 Fox Talbot Museum ms LA46–78.

2 John Vivian Hughes, *The Wealthiest Commoner: C.R.M. Talbot*, Talbot Printing Co Ltd, 1978, p 10.

3 *Ibid*, p 7.

4 *Ibid*, p 16.

5 W C Rogers, *A Pictorial History of Swansea*, Gomer Press, 1981, p 156.

6 W C Rogers, 'Jones of the Plas, Verandah [*sic*] , and Heathfield Lodge', Swansea, AMs, p 11.

7 Royal Institution of South Wales, Swansea, AMs.

8 *South Walian* (Swansea), December 1902, p 186.

9 Dr Roderick Howell, 'The Rev. Calvert Jones as an Artist', AMsS.

10 Fox Talbot Museum ms LA46–78.

11 Fox Talbot Museum ms LA39–16.

12 Fox Talbot Museum ms LA41–35.

13 William Henry Thornthwaite, *Photographic Manipulation*, Edward Palmer, 1843, p 34.

14 Fox Talbot Museum ms LA45–22.

15 Fox Talbot Museum ms LA45–108.

16 Fox Talbot Museum ms LA45–110.

17 Fox Talbot Museum ms LA45–118.

18 Fox Talbot Museum ms LA45–134.

19 Fox Talbot Museum ms LA45–154.

20 Fox Talbot Museum ms LA46–40.

21 Fox Talbot Museum ms LA46–76.

22 Fox Talbot Museum ms LA46–81.

23 Fox Talbot Museum ms LA47–37.

24 Calvert Jones, 'On a Binocular Camera', *Journal of the Photographic Society of London*, I, 1854, pp 60–61.

25 W C Rogers, *op cit* (note 6), p 6.

26 Fox Talbot Museum ms LA53–24.

*Hippolyte Bayard had also invented a direct positive photographic process on paper, but preferred the calotype and the daguerreotype to his own invention.

# PLATES

PLATE 1

*Man seated in doorway*

(cat. no. PI4)

PLATE 2

*Two figures by a house wall*

(cat. no. PG5)

PLATE 3
*Man seated on steps*
(cat. no. PE20)

PLATE 4

*Old Bakery Street, Valetta*

(cat. no. SVM38)

PLATE 5
*Swansea Castle*
(cat. no. CM1)

PLATE 6

*Windmill*

(cat. no. SVM26)

PLATE 7

*York Minster*

(cat. no. CC20)

PLATE 8

*Piazza Vittoriosa*

(cat. no. SVM19)

PLATE 9
*'38, Piazza Vittoriosa'*
(listed in appendix A4;
(cat. no. PS9)

PLATE 10

*'70 Temple of Vesta and R . . . , Rome'* inscribed

(cat. no. AR5)

PLATE 11

*'67, Colosseum Rome 2nd View'*, inscribed

(cat. no. AR8)

PLATE 12

*Bridge and business establishments, sign BROWN CONGREVE MATCH*

(cat. no. SVB4)

PLATE 13

*'SHIP AND HOUSE JOINER, J SULLY BLOCK AND PUMP MAKER'*

(cat. no. SVB9)

PLATE 14

*'House of the Tragic Poet'*

inscribed verso, with seated figure

(cat. no. AP2)

PLATE 15

*Man and woman by arch*

(cat. no. PG6)

PLATE 16

*Orangery at Margam Park*

(cat. no. CM11)

PLATE 17
*Two figures under ivy-covered tree*
(cat. no. PE32)

PLATE 18

*Man beside ship in dry dock*

(cat. no. PE17)

PLATE 19

*Women on deck of ship in dry dock*

(cat. no. PE19)

PLATE 20

*Rowboat ashore*

(cat. no. HS97)

PLATE 21

*Grounded vessel with sails unfurled*

(cat. no. HS2)

PLATE 22

*Wharf view with figures*

(cat. no. HS47)

PLATE 23

*Head and bows of* 'Ellen Simpson' *barque*

(cat. no. HS5)

PLATE 24

*Rigging*

(cat. no. HMSS9)

PLATE 25
*Prow of docked ship*
(cat. no. HS24)

PLATE 26

*Grounded sailing ships*

(cat. no. HS14)

PLATE 27

*Three-masted ship,* 'Shannon', *capstan in foreground*

(cat. no. HS36)

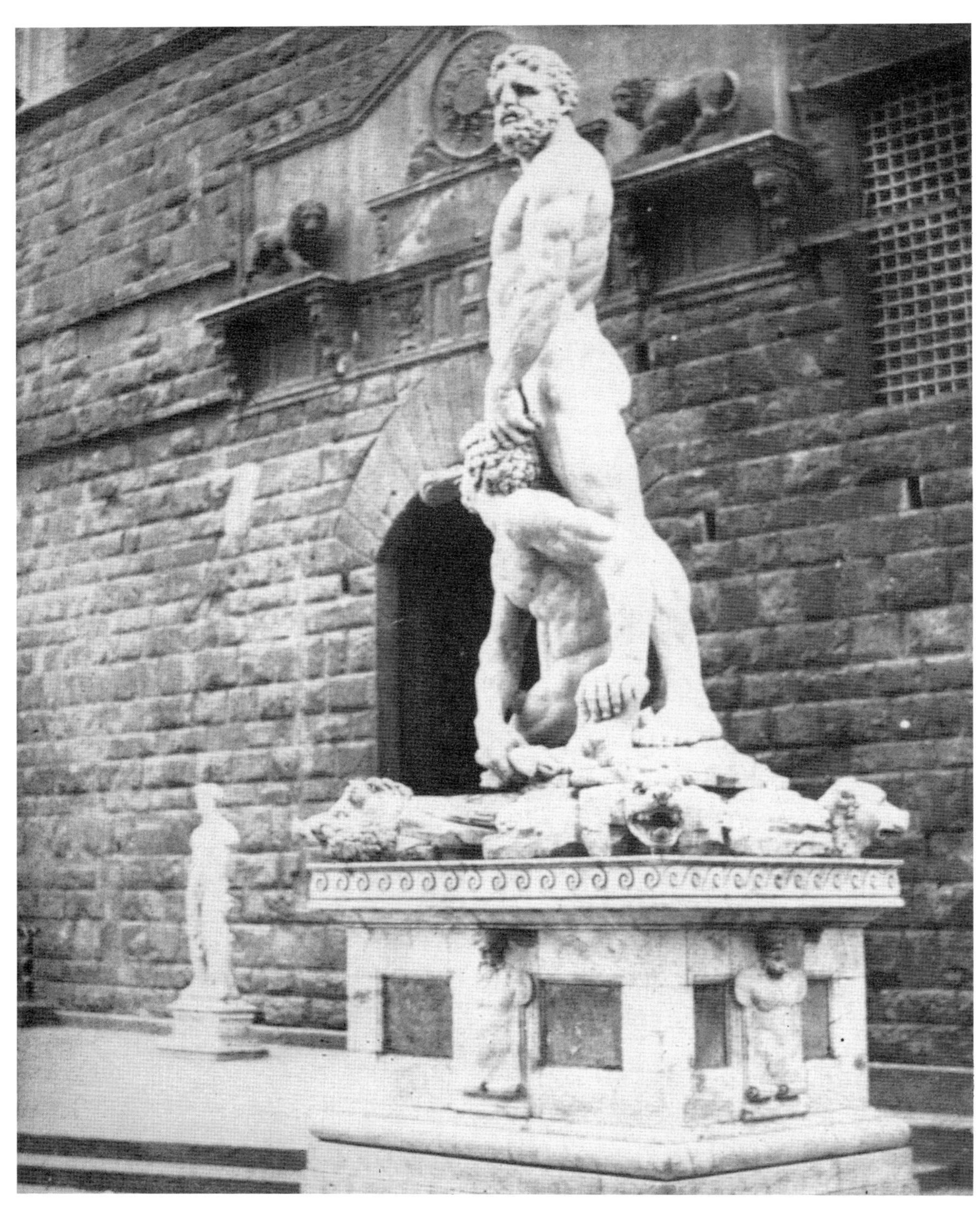

PLATE 28

*Statue in Florence*

(cat. no. PS8)

PLATE 29
*Dolphin fountain*
(cat. no. PS2)

PLATE 30

*Garden implements*

(cat. no. S8)

# CATALOGUE

## *Notes*

Letters and numbers preceding headings or titles are the reference numbers for this catalogue.

Quoted descriptions or titles are taken from the print or negative, or from the list sent by Jones to London on 26 March 1847: others are the author's.

The source of each reproduced image is printed in capital letters. Letters and numbers following the source are the source's accession number. All Science Museum images are inventoried as a collection under inventory numbers 1937–370 and 1937–371. The best-preserved image is reproduced: other sources of the same image are also quoted, with accession details.

Dimensions are shown in centimetres. Width precedes height. Since image and sheet are often irregular, all measurements are taken at the central axis.

Positive images are shown except when the image is very faint or when only the negative is available.

All images are calotypes unless otherwise noted, and the positives are salt prints.

## MARINE
*Harbours and Ships*
**(HS)**

**HS1 Small boats at low tide in Swansea harbour**
NATIONAL MARITIME MUSEUM 4405, 1 positive: image 20.9 × 16.1 cm, trimmed, faint
Royal Institution of South Wales C743, 1 positive: 20.9 × 16.1 cm, trimmed; initialled and dated 'CRJ 1846'
Science Museum IM 17, 2 positives: sheet 24.7 × 19.5 cm; image 21.1 × 16.2 cm
Hans P Kraus Jr Collection, *Sun Pictures*, Catalogue IV, 32, 1 positive: sheet 21.7 × 16.7 cm; image 21.1 × 16.2 cm, inscribed 'I HW' in ink verso intensified by Harold White

**HS2 Grounded vessel with sails unfurled**
NATIONAL MARITIME MUSEUM 4218, 1 positive: sheet 22.8 × 18.6 cm, image 21.9 × 18.2 cm
Royal Photographic Society, negative image 21.2 × 16.3 cm, trimmed, waxed
Royal Institution of South Wales C749, 1 positive: 21.1 × 16.2 cm, dated 1847, trimmed

**HS3 Three grounded vessels, Swansea harbour**
NATIONAL MARITIME MUSEUM C 3599, 1 positive: sheet 22.5 × 18.5 cm; image 22.3 × 18.3 cm; negative 20.3 × 16.4 cm
Royal Institution of South Wales C 748, 1 positive: image 20.3 × 16.2 cm, trimmed, 'Mary St. Ives 1847'
Division of Photographic History, Smithsonian Institution 67.172.7, 1 positive: sheet 24.7 × 19.8 cm; image 20.4 × 16.4 cm

**HS4 'Aurora'**
ROYAL INSTITUTION OF SOUTH WALES C 741, 1 positive: image 21.5 × 16.6 cm, trimmed, faint image; initialled and dated 'CRJ 1846' Dutch galliot lying at wharf
National Maritime Museum C 3600, 1 positive: sheet 22.5 × 18.5 cm; image 22.5 × 18.5; negative 21.5 × 16.6 cm; trimmed, inscribed '18 Aurora'

**HS5 'Ellen Simpson'**
NATIONAL MARITIME MUSEUM B 9162, 1 positive: image 21.0 × 16.2 cm, trimmed, brilliant print
Science Museum, negative 21.2 × 16.5 cm
Science Museum, Number 14 'Head and bows of "Ellen Simpson" barque' in *Talbotypes or Sun Pictures* by Nicholaas Henneman, 1847; Andre Jammes Collection, attributed to WHF Talbot

**HS6 'Copper Ore Vessel', Swansea**
NATIONAL MARITIME MUSEUM 4219/C2257, 1 positive: sheet 22.4 × 18.6 cm; image 20.2 × 16.2 cm; negative 20.3 × 16.2 cm, trimmed, waxed
Science Museum number 16 in *Talbotypes or Sun Pictures* by Nicholaas Henneman, 1847, 1 positive: image 20 × 15.9 cm, trimmed
Royal Institution of South Wales C 738, 1 positive: image 20.4 × 16.1 cm, trimmed
Lacock Abbey Collection LA 507, 1 positive: sheet 23.1 × 18.5 cm; image 20.5 × 16.3 cm

**HS7 Vessel at low tide**
NATIONAL MARITIME MUSEUM 3758/C5373, 1 positive: sheet 8.8 × 6.8 cm; image 7.1 × 6.3 cm; negative 7.1 × 6.3, trimmed, waxed

**HS8 Paddle-wheel ship lying along dock, verso 'Admiralty steam packet'**
NATIONAL MARITIME MUSEUM 4404, 2 positives: sheet 22.7 × 18.7 cm; image 20 × 14.8 cm

**HS9 Brig and barque aground, Swansea**
NATIONAL MARITIME MUSEUM 4606/C5374, 1 positive: image 16.2 × 20.8 cm, trimmed, torn lower left corner, top corners clipped; negative 16.2 × 21 cm, trimmed
Science Museum Number 15 'Brig and Barque Aground, Swansea' in *Talbotypes or Sun Pictures* by Nicholaas Henneman, 1847 (marked in NMM 'Head and bow of the Ellen Simpson')
Royal Institution of South Wales C 746, 1 positive: image 16.2 × 20.8 cm, trimmed

**HS10 French brig, aground**
NATIONAL MARITIME MUSEUM 4605/C2254, 1 positive: sheet 24.5 × 19.6 cm; image 21.4 × 16.6 cm; negative 21.4 × 16.6 cm
Science Museum, Number 13 'French Brig, Aground' in *Talbotypes or Sun Pictures* by Nicholaas Henneman, 1847
Royal Institution of South Wales C 751, 1 positive: image 21.5 × 16.6 cm, trimmed

**HS11 Grounded boats in harbour**
NATIONAL MARITIME MUSEUM A 6087, 1 positive: sheet 22.7 × 18.2 cm; image 22.5 × 18.2 cm, faded on lower left; verso in pencil 'Swansea 1845?'

**HS12 Ship moored at dock**
NATIONAL MARITIME MUSEUM A 6082, 1 positive: sheet 22.9 × 18.5 cm; image 22.6 × 18 cm; faint image, pencil verso 'Swansea 1846'

**HS13 Three-masted ship aground, Swansea**
SCIENCE MUSEUM, 1 positive: sheet 12.6 × 9.9 cm; image 10.5 × 8.7 cm
National Maritime Museum C 3602, 1 positive: sheet 12.1 × 9.6 cm; image 10.5 × 8.7 cm; negative 11.3 × 9.2 cm
Royal Photographic Society, 1 of 4 positives on single sheet 25 × 19.6 cm; image 10.5 × 8.7 cm

**HS14 Grounded sailing ships**
NATIONAL MARITIME MUSEUM A 6088, 1 positive: sheet 23.5 × 19.7 cm; image 23 × 18.5 cm
Division of Photographic History, Smithsonian Institution, 67.172.19, 1 positive: sheet 26.3 × 30.3 cm, inscribed; image 25.3 × 19.2 cm

**HS15 Docked ships afloat, inscribed '579'**
NATIONAL MARITIME MUSEUM C 3598, negative 20.8 × 16.3 cm, trimmed, waxed

**HS16 Swansea harbour, ships unloading at Cobra Wharf**
NATIONAL MARITIME MUSEUM C 2258, negative 21.3 × 16.4 cm, trimmed, waxed
Royal Institution of South Wales C 742, 1 positive: image 20.8 × 16.6 cm, faint; initialled and dated 'CRJ, 1846'

**HS17 Five moored ships with city in background**
NATIONAL MARITIME MUSEUM C 2255, negative 19.5 × 16 cm, faint image

**HS18 Dock scene with barrels**
NATIONAL MARITIME MUSEUM 3601 A, negative 17.8 × 16.3 cm, trimmed

**HS19 Dock scene with barrels**
NATIONAL MARITIME MUSEUM 3601 B, negative 17.1 × 16.6 cm, soft focus; also attributed to WHF Talbot

**HS20 Swansea harbour: discharging ships at Cobra Wharf, ship right 'Mary Dugdale'**
NATIONAL MARITIME MUSEUM C 5371/4603, negative 21.1 × 16.5 cm, trimmed, waxed
Royal Institution of South Wales C 740, 1 positive: image 20.8 × 16.5 cm, trimmed, initialled and dated 'CRJ 1846'

**HS21 Two sailing boats, S4, S7 Neptune**
NATIONAL MARITIME MUSEUM C 3594, negative 20.7 × 16 cm, trimmed, waxed

**HS22 Two bows**
ROYAL INSTITUTION OF SOUTH WALES C 750, 1 positive: image 21.2 × 16.3 cm, trimmed
National Maritime Museum C 2253, negative 21.2 × 16.6 cm, trimmed

**HS23 Many moored ships with dinghy in foreground**
NATIONAL MARITIME MUSEUM C 2256, negative 21.3 × 16.1 cm

**HS24 Prow of docked ship**
VICTORIA AND ALBERT MUSEUM Ph 36–1983, 1 positive: image 20.1 × 17.9 cm, trimmed

**HS25 Prow and transom of two docked ships**
VICTORIA AND ALBERT MUSEUM Ph 41–1983, 1 positive: image 23.6 × 17.5 cm, trimmed

**HS26 Ship in Bristol Estuary**
VICTORIA AND ALBERT MUSEUM Ph 45–1983, 1 positive: image 17.8 × 21.8 cm, trimmed

**HS27 Dock wall with chained dinghy**
VICTORIA AND ALBERT MUSEUM Ph 48–1983, 1 positive: image 21.5 × 17.8 cm, trimmed

**HS28 Acheman Wharf, Bristol**
VICTORIA AND ALBERT MUSEUM Ph 58–1983, 1 positive: image 22.1 × 18 cm, trimmed

**HS29 Figurehead on ship in dry dock**
VICTORIA AND ALBERT MUSEUM Ph 60–1983, 1 positive: image 22.3 × 18.8 cm, trimmed

**HS30 Grounded ships in tidal estuary**
VICTORIA AND ALBERT MUSEUM Ph 99–1983, 1 positive: image 22.4 × 17.8 cm, trimmed

**HS31 Ships at dockside, carriages in background**
VICTORIA AND ALBERT MUSEUM Ph 101–1983, 1 positive: image 22.8 × 18.6 cm, trimmed, faint

**HS32 Long view of ship and harbour**
VICTORIA AND ALBERT MUSEUM Ph 103–1983, 1 positive: image 22.2 × 17.3 cm, trimmed, very faint

**HS33 Long view of harbour, grounded hulls**
VICTORIA AND ALBERT MUSEUM Ph 113–1983, 1 positive: image 23 × 18.1 cm, trimmed

**HS34 Prow of sailing ship with two-stack steamer**
VICTORIA AND ALBERT MUSEUM Ph 116–1983, 1 positive: image 23.2 × 17.8 cm, trimmed

**HS35 'Shannon' with open ports at dock**
VICTORIA AND ALBERT MUSEUM Ph 118–1983, 1 positive: image 22.7 × 17.7 cm, trimmed

**HS36 Three-masted ship, 'Shannon', capstan in foreground**
VICTORIA AND ALBERT MUSEUM Ph 121–1983, 1 positive: image 23 × 18.7 cm, trimmed

**HS37 'Shannon'**
VICTORIA AND ALBERT MUSEUM Ph 126–1983, 1 positive: image 22.5 × 18.6 cm, trimmed

**HS38 Two ships with sails unfurled**
ROYAL INSTITUTION OF SOUTH WALES C 739, 1 positive: image 20.6 × 16.5 cm, trimmed, very faint
LACOCK ABBEY COLLECTION LA 2038 NB1, 1 positive: image 21.2 × 16.5 cm, trimmed

**HS39 Ships aground**
ROYAL INSTITUTION OF SOUTH WALES C 744, 1 positive: image 21.3 × 16.6 cm, faint

**HS40 Two-masted vessel**

ROYAL INSTITUTION OF SOUTH WALES C 745, 1 positive: image 21.2 × 16.6 cm, trimmed

**HS41 Three vessels aground at dock**
ROYAL PHOTOGRAPHIC SOCIETY 112, negative 21.5 × 16.4 cm, trimmed

**HS42 Two vessels**
ROYAL PHOTOGRAPHIC SOCIETY 111, negative 21 × 15.8 cm, trimmed

**HS43 The New Inn on tidal estuary**
VICTORIA AND ALBERT MUSEUM Ph 53–1983, 1 positive: image 17.5 × 22 cm, trimmed

**HS44 Tidal estuary with beached boat, possibly Bristol**
VICTORIA AND ALBERT MUSEUM Ph 54–1983, 1 positive: image 17.6 × 22 cm, trimmed

**HS45 Long view of docked vessel afloat**
LACOCK ABBEY COLLECTION LA 497, 1 positive: sheet 19 × 22.8 cm; image 16.9 × 16.7 cm, trimmed
National Maritime Museum A 6089, 1 positive: sheet 22.8 × 18.5 cm; image 17.1 × 16.5 cm, trimmed
Science Museum, negative 17.3 × 16.3 cm, trimmed

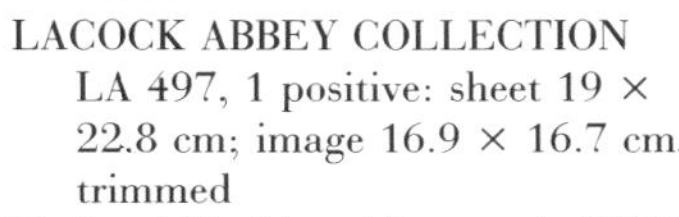

**HS46 On board the 'Viago'**
SCIENCE MUSEUM, 1 positive: sheet 22.5 × 18.6 cm; image 21.9 × 16.8 cm

**HS47 Wharf view with figures**
LACOCK ABBEY COLLECTION LA 500, 1 positive: sheet 22.8 × 18.7 cm; image 20.1 × 16.9 cm
National Maritime Museum c 3595, negative 20.1 × 16.9 cm, trimmed

**HS48 Dutch galliot, Swansea**
SCIENCE MUSEUM, 2 positives: sheet 24.6 × 19.8 cm; image 22 × 16.8 cm

**HS49 Long view of boats ashore**
SCIENCE MUSEUM, 1 positive: sheet 11.6 × 9.2 cm; image 10.6 × 8.5 cm

**HS50 Side-wheel vessel**
ROYAL PHOTOGRAPHIC SOCIETY 113, negative 20.1 × 15 cm, trimmed

**HS51 Docked vessels near suspension bridge**
SCIENCE MUSEUM, negative 17.3 × 8.8 cm, trimmed; doubtful attribution

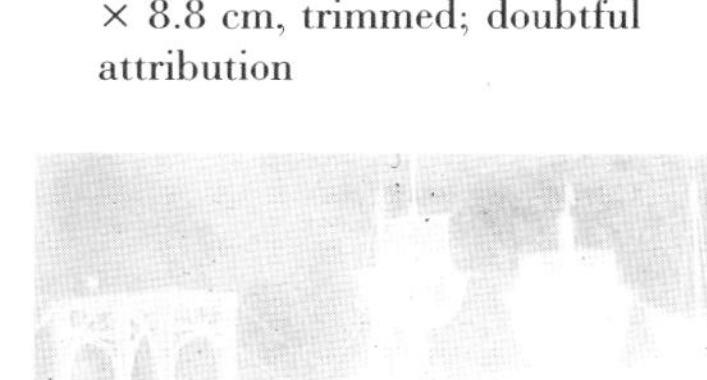

**HS52 Docked vessels near suspension bridge**
NATIONAL MARITIME MUSEUM C 3604, negative 15.5 × 8.5 cm, severely trimmed, faint image; doubtful attribution

**HS53 Pilot boat and fishing smack, Swansea**
HANS P KRAUS JR COLLECTION, *Sun Pictures*, Catalogue IV, 27, 1 positive: sheet 23.9 × 18.8 cm; image 22.6 × 18.5 cm; inscribed 'I HW' in ink verso, intensified by Harold White

**HS54 Swansea harbour**
ROYAL INSTITUTION OF SOUTH WALES C 737, 1 positive: 17.5 × 19.3 cm; trimmed

**HS55 Swansea harbour**
ROYAL INSTITUTION OF SOUTH WALES C 754, 1 positive: image 16.5 × 19.3 cm, trimmed

**HS56 Swansea harbour**
ROYAL INSTITUTION OF SOUTH WALES C 755, 1 positive: image 15.6 × 16.2 cm, trimmed

**HS57 '45 Bay of Baia (joins 46 at xx)'**
SCIENCE MUSEUM, 6 positives: sheet 22.7 × 18.6 cm; image 22.1 × 16.7 cm
Lacock Abbey Collection LA 152, 1 positive: sheet 23.7 × 19.2 cm; image 22.2 × 16.8 cm

**HS58 '46 Baia (joins 45 at xx)'**
SCIENCE MUSEUM, 1 positive: sheet 22.9 × 18.2 cm; image 22 × 16.9 cm
National Maritime Museum C 3605B, 1 positive: 22 × 16.9 cm
National Museum of Photography, Film and Television m 3786 j, 1 positive: sheet 22.9 × 18.2 cm; image 22 × 16.9 cm; watermark J. Whatman 1846.

**HS59 Five beached small sailing boats, Naples**
SCIENCE MUSEUM, 1 positive: sheet 24.6 × 19.7 cm; image 20.5 × 16.4 cm, trimmed
National Maritime Museum C3597, 1 positive: sheet 24.7 × 19.5 cm; image 20.5 × 16.4 cm, trimmed; verso in pencil 'Naples 1846'; negative 20.5 × 16.4 cm, trimmed, waxed
Lacock Abbey Collection LA 2020 NB1, 1 positive: image 20.5 × 16.4 cm, trimmed, in album
National Museum of Photography, Film and Television, 1 positive: sheet 22.4 × 18.2 cm; image 20.6 × 16.5 cm
Hans P Kraus Jr Collection, *Sun Pictures*, Catalogue IV, 20, 1 positive: sheet 21.7 × 18.3 cm; image 20.4 × 16.4 cm

**HS60 Maltese sailing boat**
NATIONAL MARITIME MUSEUM 4403, 1 positive: sheet 23.3 × 16.8 cm; image 20.6 × 15.6 cm, trimmed
Science Museum, negative 20.5 × 15.5 cm
Lacock Abbey Collection LA 2016 NB1, 1 positive: image 21.6 × 15.5 cm, trimmed

**HS61 '22. On the Marina, Naples'**
NATIONAL MARITIME MUSEUM C 3605 (A), 1 positive: sheet 23.7 × 19.3 cm; image 22.5 × 18.5 cm

**HS62 Long view with windmill, 'Several views of Senglea: From the Marine'**
NATIONAL MARITIME MUSEUM C 3590, negative 21.4 × 16.2 cm

**HS63 Long view with double campanile in distance**
NATIONAL MARITIME MUSEUM C 3591, negative 19.9 × 14.5 cm, trimmed, waxed

**HS64 Long view with boom and double campanile in distance**
NATIONAL MARITIME MUSEUM C 3592, negative 19.2 × 16 cm, trimmed, waxed

**HS65 Moored ship with longboat on dock**
NATIONAL MARITIME MUSEUM C 5372 negative 10.6 × 8.5 cm, trimmed, corners clipped

**HS66 Three boats ashore**
VICTORIA AND ALBERT MUSEUM Ph 110–1983, 1 positive: image 21.8 × 17.5 cm, trimmed

**HS67 Beached boats**
VICTORIA AND ALBERT MUSEUM Ph 122–1983, 1 positive: image 22.8 × 17.5 cm

**HS68 Bay of Baia**
LACOCK ABBEY COLLECTION LA 161, 1 positive: sheet 24.1 × 19.3 cm; image 21.4 × 16.7 cm, trimmed
Science Museum, negative 21.4 × 16.7 cm

**HS69 '40 Ste. Lucia, Naples (joins 41 at xx)'**
ROYAL LIBRARY OF COPENHAGEN 1967 – 337/4 ch 86, 1 positive: sheet 18.5 × 22.5 cm; image 16.4 × 22 cm
Lacock Abbey Collection LA 358, 1 positive: sheet 17.4 × 22.8 cm; image 16.8 × 21.8 cm
Science Museum, 1 positive: sheet 19.2 × 23.8 cm; image 16.7 × 21.6 cm; negative 18.5 × 22.5 cm, inked sky
Division of Photographic History, Smithsonian Institution 67.172.60, 1 positive: sheet 18.6 × 22.4 cm; image 16.8 × 22 cm

**HS70 '41 (xx) Ste. Lucia, Naples from Villa de Roma Hotel (joins 40 at xx)'**
SCIENCE MUSEUM, 2 positives: sheet 22.4 × 21.8 cm; image 18.6 × 16.2 cm; negative 22.3 × 18.8 cm, inked sky

**HS71 Small sailing boat in shallow water**
SCIENCE MUSEUM, 2 positives: sheet 11.6 × 9.1 cm; image 8.8 × 7.7 cm; negative 8.8 × 7.7 cm, waxed, corners clipped

**HS72 Small boat**
SCIENCE MUSEUM, 1 positive: sheet 10.9 × 9.6 cm; image 9.5 × 7.5 cm, very faint

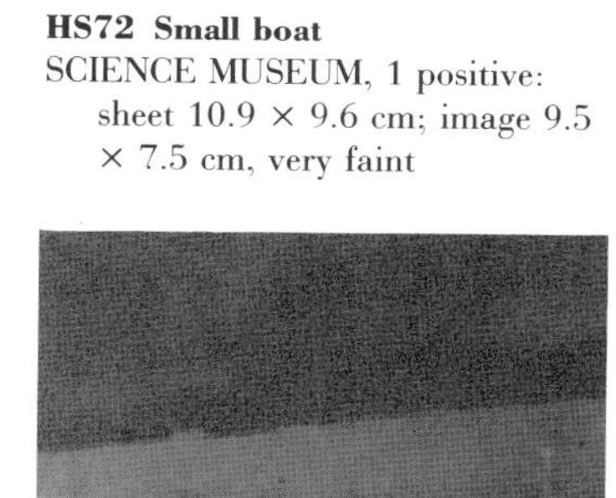

**HS73 Small boat**
SCIENCE MUSEUM, negative 9.5 × 7.5 cm, trimmed, waxed

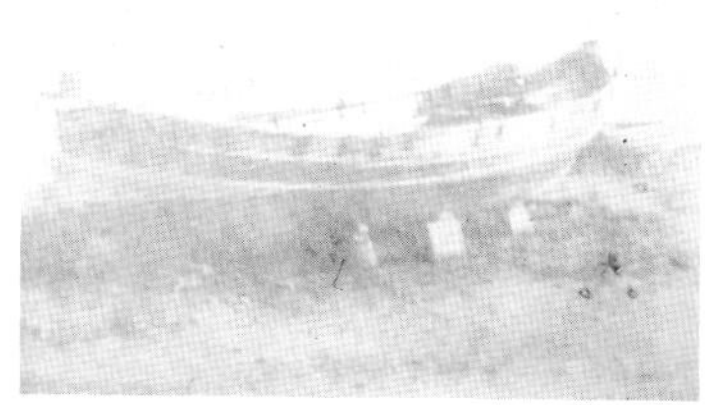

**HS74 Single beached boat, no rigging**
SCIENCE MUSEUM, 1 positive: sheet 11.3 × 9.6 cm; image 10 × 8.5 cm, trimmed

**HS75 Two long boats ashore, ship masts in background**
SCIENCE MUSEUM, negative 9.7 × 7.8 cm, trimmed

**HS76 Small masted boats ashore**
SCIENCE MUSEUM, 1 positive: sheet 11.2 × 9.4 cm; image 10.4 × 8.6 cm, trimmed; negative 9.7 × 8.3 cm, further trimmed after printing

**HS77 Bow of boat (joiner)**
SCIENCE MUSEUM, 3 positives: sheet 11.1 × 9.4 cm; image 10.1 × 8.4 cm, trimmed; negative 10.1 × 8.4 cm

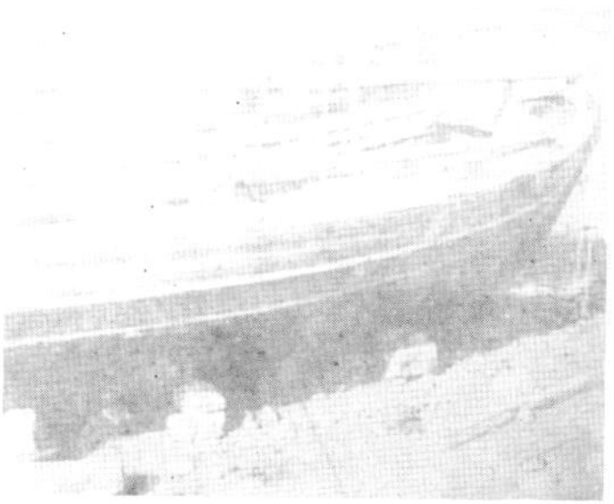

**HS78 Stern of boat '11' (joins HS77 above)**
SCIENCE MUSEUM, 2 positives: sheet 11.3 × 9.1 cm; image 10.6 × 8.5 cm; negative 9.9 × 8.1 cm

**HS79 Two Maltese boats**
SCIENCE MUSEUM, 5 positives: sheet 11.3 × 11 cm; image 10.5 × 8.5 cm, trimmed; negative 10.5 × 8.5 cm

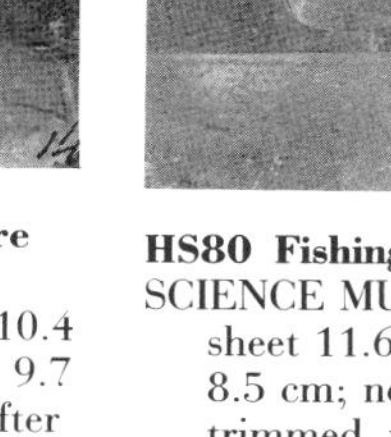

**HS80 Fishing boats ashore**
SCIENCE MUSEUM, 1 positive: sheet 11.6 × 10 cm; image 10 × 8.5 cm; negative 10 × 8.5 cm, trimmed, waxed; 2 positives: image 9.5 × 7.8 cm, trimmed

**HS81 Boat alongside wall**
SCIENCE MUSEUM, negative 10 × 8.5 cm, trimmed

**HS82 Capstan on the Marine, probably no. 5 listed in Small Talbotypes**
SCIENCE MUSEUM, negative 10 × 8.3 cm

**HS83 Seawall and lighthouse, Malta**
SCIENCE MUSEUM, negative 20.3 × 16 cm
International Museum of Photography at George Eastman House 81:2850:4; 1 positive: image 20.1 × 15.7 cm

**HS84 Valetta harbour**
SCIENCE MUSEUM, negative 20.2 × 15.9 cm, trimmed

**HS85 'Valetta, Malta'**
SCIENCE MUSEUM, negative 22.3 × 18.5 cm, poor condition

**HS86 Ship chandler at Valetta harbour**
SCIENCE MUSEUM, negative 21.1 × 15.6 cm

**HS87 Maltese seafront, wall and campanile**
SCIENCE MUSEUM, negative 20.1 × 16.3 cm

**HS88 Street fronting on dock**
SCIENCE MUSEUM, negative 20.7 × 15.6 cm

**HS89 'Fort Tigne, Malta paper badly washed after being nitrated'**
SCIENCE MUSEUM, negative 22.4 × 17 cm; very poor condition, not CRJ's handwriting, doubtful attribution

**HS90 'Porta delle Bombe, Malta bad gallic acid'**
SCIENCE MUSEUM, negative 22.5 × 18.5 cm; very poor condition, not CRJ's handwriting, doubtful attribution

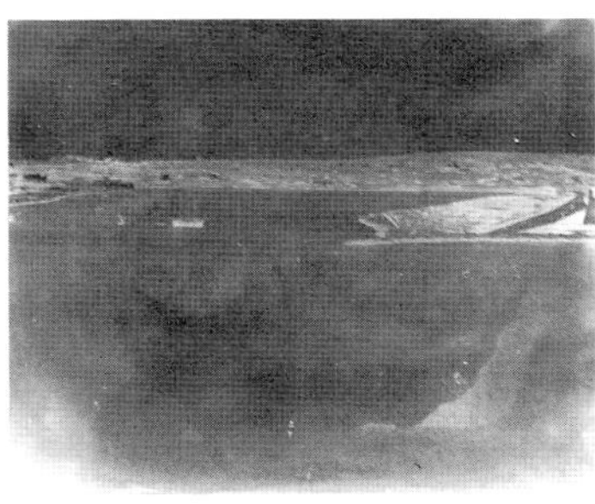

**HS91 Long view of harbour**
SCIENCE MUSEUM, negative 22.7 × 18.7 cm, dense

**HS92 Long view Valetta**
SCIENCE MUSEUM, 1 positive: sheet 22.1 × 18.2 cm; image 21.6 × 17.6 cm; negative 22.4 × 17.6 cm

**HS93 Long view with public building above harbour**
SCIENCE MUSEUM, negative 21.5 × 16.4 cm, trimmed, inked sky

**HS94 'View of the Chiatamone, Naples' inscribed on negative**
SCIENCE MUSEUM, 8 positives: sheet 25 × 19.5 cm; image 20.3 × 16.1 cm; negative 20.3 × 16.1 cm, trimmed, waxed

**HS95 Narrow peninsula between two bays**
SCIENCE MUSEUM, negative 22.7 × 18.8 cm, poor condition

**HS96 High view of Valetta harbour**
SCIENCE MUSEUM, 1 positive: sheet 23.7 × 18.9 cm; 20.8 × 15.6 cm, very faded; negative 20.8 × 15.6 cm, tabs

**HS97 Rowboat ashore**
SCIENCE MUSEUM, negative 21.7 × 16.8 cm

**HS98 Cannon balls on wall high above harbour**
SCIENCE MUSEUM, negative 19.4 × 15.8 cm, trimmed, waxed, dense

**HS99 Seafront with ruin, Naples**
SCIENCE MUSEUM, 2 positives: sheet 22.5 × 18.7 cm; image 20.6 × 15.5 cm; negative 20.6 × 15.5 cm, trimmed

**HS100 Castle at Baia**
SCIENCE MUSEUM, negative 21 × 16.2 cm, trimmed, inked sky

**HS101 Native boats ashore, oculus on boat number 72**
SCIENCE MUSEUM, 1 positive: sheet 23.2 × 18.7 cm; image 20.2 × 15.8 cm; negative 20.2 × 15.8 cm, trimmed

**HS102 '44 From the Hotel dei Stranieri (?) Chietamone, Naples, 1846'**
SCIENCE MUSEUM, 1 positive: 21.3 × 16.1 cm, trimmed, waxed
Sotheby's, London, Catalogue No. 57, 1 positive: sheet 23.5 × 19.2 cm; image 21.8 × 16.8 cm

**HS103 Naples**
SCIENCE MUSEUM, negative 21 × 16.2 cm, trimmed

**HS104 Naples**
SCIENCE MUSEUM, 3 positives: sheet 22.1 × 18.7 cm; image 20 × 15.5 cm; negative 20 × 15.5 cm, trimmed

**HS105 Naples**
SCIENCE MUSEUM, negative 21.2 × 16.2 cm, trimmed

**HS106 Seafront Naples**
SCIENCE MUSEUM, 1 positive: sheet 24.5 × 19.5 cm; image 21.5 × 16.3 cm; faint inscription '. . . naples'

**HS107 Naples**
SCIENCE MUSEUM, negative 20.4 × 16.1 cm, trimmed

**HS108 Bay of Baia, rotunda and capstans**
SCIENCE MUSEUM, negative 21.3 × 16.2 cm, trimmed, tabbed

**HS109 Immacolatella, figures on steps to harbour**
SCIENCE MUSEUM, 6 positives: sheet 24.9 × 19.8 cm, image 21.2 × 16.2 cm; negative 21.2 × 16.2 cm, trimmed, waxed

**HS110 '20 Naples from the . . . ' inscribed on negative**
SCIENCE MUSEUM, negative 20.6 × 16 cm, trimmed, waxed

**HS111 Naples**
SCIENCE MUSEUM, 1 positive: sheet 23.8 × 19.3 cm; image 21.1 × 16.9 cm

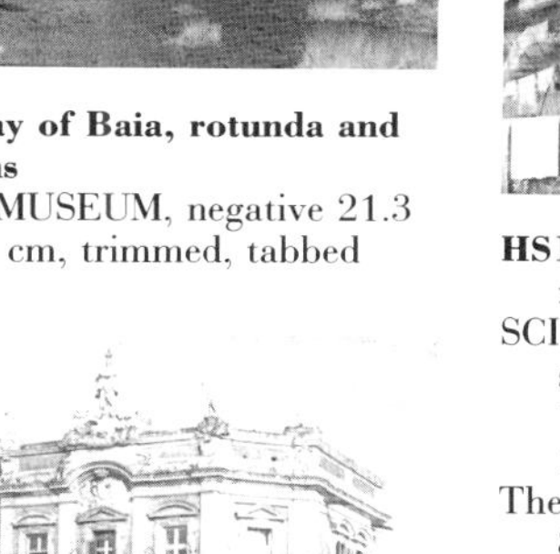

**HS112 '42. Ste. Lucia joins 43 at xx Naples'**
SCIENCE MUSEUM, 2 positives: sheet 18.2 × 22.5 cm; image 16.9 × 21.3 cm; negative 22.4 × 18.4 cm
The J Paul Getty Museum 84.XP.921.7, 1 positive: sheet 18.8 × 22.5 cm; image 16.9 × 21.3 cm
Hans P Kraus Jr Collection, *Sun Pictures*, Catalogue I 13, 1 positive: sheet 18.2 × 23.2 cm; image 16.9 × 21.3 cm

**HS113 '43 Ste. Lucia (joins 42 at xx)'**
SCIENCE MUSEUM, 3 positives: sheet 17.8 × 22.6 cm; image 16.8 × 21.7 cm; negative 18.6 × 22.4 cm
Division of Photographic History, Smithsonian Institution 67.172.5, 1 positive: sheet 18.5 × 22.4 cm; image 16.8 × 21.7 cm
Hans P Kraus Jr Collection, *Sun Pictures*, Catalogue I 13, 1 positive: sheet 19.1 × 23.8 cm; image 16.8 × 21.5 cm
Robert Hershkowitz Ltd, 1 positive: sheet 18.7 × 22.4 cm; image 16.8 × 21.7 cm
The J Paul Getty Museum 85.XM.253.1, 1 positive: sheet 19 × 23.6 cm; image 16.8 × 21.7 cm

**HS114 Porta della Ripetta**
LACOCK ABBEY COLLECTION 2018 NB1, 1 positive: image 21.2 × 16.3 cm, trimmed
Science Museum, negative 21.1 × 16.5 cm

**HS115 'Castallo dell'Oro, Naples, May 1846 from villa . . . ', inscribed**
SCIENCE MUSEUM, 3 positives: sheet 23.8 × 19.8 cm; image 21.7 × 15.8 cm; watermark, Chafford Mills 1842

**HS116 Buildings fronting harbour**
SCIENCE MUSEUM, negative 21.7 × 15.9 cm, trimmed, waxed

**HS117 Ship afloat, blurred masts**
NATIONAL MARITIME MUSEUM 3603, negative 19.5 × 14 cm, trimmed, faint image; doubtful attribution

**HS118 'View of Bay of Naples from Spada', inscribed**
HARRISON D HORBLIT COLLECTION, 1 positive: sheet 22.4 × 18.5 cm; image 21.2 × 15.7 cm, faint image

## HMS 'Superb' (HMSS)

**HMSS1 Officer and sailor on deck of 'Superb'**
NATIONAL MARITIME MUSEUM 3596, 1 positive: sheet 11.6 × 8.7 cm; image 10.1 × 8.3 cm; verso in pencil 'Poop of Superb 1845'
Science Museum, 1 positive: sheet 10.4 × 8.6 cm; image 10.1 × 8.3 cm
Hans P Kraus Jr Collection, *Sun Pictures*, Catalogue III, 51–52, attributed to Henneman or Talbot, 1 positive: sheet 11.4 × 8.9 cm; image 10.1 × 8.3 cm; negative 10.1 × 8.3 cm

**HMSS2 Officer and sailor on deck of 'Superb'**
HANS P KRAUS JR COLLECTION, *Sun Pictures*, Catalogue III, 53, attributed to Henneman or Talbot; 1 positive: sheet 22.5 × 18.6 cm; image 20.2 × 16.5 cm
National Maritime Museum C 3596, negative 20.1 × 16.4 cm, trimmed

**HMSS3 Three sailors on deck of 'Superb'**
NATIONAL MARITIME MUSEUM C 3573, 1 positive: sheet 11.1 × 9.2 cm; image 9.2 × 8.1 cm, corners clipped; verso in pencil 'Looking toward the bows from quarterdeck of Superb in 1845 showing boom boats stowed three abreast and main mast 4′ thick'
Science Museum, 1 positive: sheet 10.6 × 9 cm; image 9.2 × 8.1 cm, corners clipped

**HMSS4 Three sailors on deck of 'Superb'**
NATIONAL MARITIME MUSEUM C 3593, negative 20.4 × 16.8 cm, trimmed, waxed

**HMSS5 Sailors and officers on deck of 'Superb'**
NATIONAL MARITIME MUSEUM C 3587/C 3587, 1 positive: sheet 22.5 × 18.6 cm; image 20.4 × 16.5 cm, varnished; verso in pencil 'View from quarter deck of "Superb"'; negative 20.4 × 16.5 cm

**HMSS6 Officer standing by cannons**
NATIONAL MARITIME MUSEUM b 9451, 1 positive: sheet 22.9 × 18.4 cm; image 20 × 16.2 cm; verso in pencil 'Starboard side of quarter deck of "Superb" 1845 (note the height of bulwarks and double breaching of guns)'
International Museum of Photography at George Eastman House 81:2850:6, 1 positive: sheet 22.8× 18.7 cm; image 20.1 × 16.3, corners clipped
Hans P Kraus Jr Collection, *Sun Pictures*, Catalogue III, 54, 1 positive: sheet 22 × 18 cm; image 20 × 16.3 cm, inscribed 'I HW' in ink verso, intensified by Harold White Division of Photographic History, Smithsonian Institution 3864.15, 1 positive: image 20.3 × 16.5 cm

**HMSS7 Officer on HMS 'Superb'**
NATIONAL MARITIME MUSEUM C 3589, negative 12.2 × 16.8 cm

**HMSS8 Deck and hatchway**
NATIONAL MARITIME MUSEUM C 2259, 1 positive: sheet 24.7 × 19.4 cm; image 21.2 × 16.7 cm, trimmed; negative 21.2 × 16.7 cm, trimmed, waxed

**HMSS9 Rigging**
NATIONAL MARITIME MUSEUM C 2260, negative 21.2 × 15.4 cm, trimmed

**HMSS10 Cannons on deck**
SCIENCE MUSEUM, 1 positive: sheet 11 × 9.9 cm; image 9.9 × 8.9 cm, faint

**HMSS11 Deck**
SCIENCE MUSEUM, 1 positive: sheet 22.6 × 18.5 cm; image 22 × 16.9 cm

## STREET VIEWS

### *Swansea*
### (SVS)

**SVS1 Street with coach office**
SCIENCE MUSEUM, negative 21.1 × 16.3 cm, trimmed, waxed

**SVS2 Farm buildings, Singleton near Swansea**
SCIENCE MUSEUM, negative 21.5 × 16.4 cm, trimmed
Science Museum: Number 9 in *Talbotypes or Sun Pictures* by Nicholaas Henneman, 1847

**SVS3 Wall with arch to farmyard**
VICTORIA AND ALBERT MUSEUM Ph 104–1983, 1 positive: image 22.5 × 18 cm, trimmed

**SVS4 Old houses**
HANS P KRAUS COLLECTION, *Sun Pictures*, Catalogue IV, 30, 1 positive: 24.7 × 19.7 cm; image 22.5 × 18.6 cm, inscribed '174' in negative

**SVS5 Shops and houses**
HARRISON D HORBLIT COLLECTION, 1 positive: image 18 × 13.2 cm, trimmed

**SVS6 Business establishments**
HARRISON D HORBLIT COLLECTION, 1 positive: image 19.7 × 15.9 cm, trimmed, watermark Turkey Mill Whatman 1841
Science Museum, negative 20.2 × 16.4 cm

### *Windsor*
### (SVW)

**SVW1 Lupton's Range, Eton College**
HANS P KRAUS JR COLLECTION, *Sun Pictures*, Catalogue IV, 25/26, 1 positive: sheet 16.9 × 18.2 cm, image 16.6 × 17.5 cm; negative 16.5 × 17.4 cm, inscribed '33' in pencil verso

### *Ludlow*
### (SVL)

**SVL1 The Feathers Inn, Ludlow**
HARRISON D HORBLIT COLLECTION, 1 positive: image 17.2 × 21.8 cm, trimmed; possibly Llewelyn

### *Dunster*
### (SVD)

**SVD1 Dunster Market Place**
ROYAL PHOTOGRAPHIC SOCIETY 171, negative sheet 21.7 × 18.8 cm; image 21.7 × 17 cm

### *Bristol*
### (SVB)

**SVB1 Narrow street, sign HALL NO. 13**
VICTORIA AND ALBERT MUSEUM Ph 39–1983, 1 positive: image 10.1 × 15.6 cm, trimmed

**SVB2 Shops, sign WHOLESALE & RETAIL**
VICTORIA AND ALBERT MUSEUM Ph 42–1983, 1 positive: image 18.5 × 25.5 cm, trimmed, faint

**SVB3 Street bordering canal, sign STOCKDALE & CO.**
VICTORIA AND ALBERT MUSEUM Ph 44–1983, 1 positive: image 21.4 × 17.5 cm; trimmed, faint image, blind stamp upper left corner

**SVB4 Bridge and businesses, sign BROWN CONGREVE MATCH**
VICTORIA AND ALBERT MUSEUM Ph 46–1983, 1 positive: image 22.5 × 17.5 cm, trimmed

**SVB5 Arch to church (same view as PE13)**
VICTORIA AND ALBERT MUSEUM Ph 47–1983, 1 positive: image 17.2 × 21.6 cm, trimmed

**SVB6 Wine Street, sign BANK**
VICTORIA AND ALBERT MUSEUM Ph 52–1983, 1 positive: image 16.5 × 21.7 cm; trimmed, blind stamp upper left corner

**SVB7 High Street**
VICTORIA AND ALBERT MUSEUM Ph 55–1983, 1 positive: image 17 × 22.1 cm, trimmed

**SVB8 Shops, sign THOMAS & SONS**
HARRISON D HORBLIT COLLECTION 20, 1 positive: image 17.6 × 22.6 cm, trimmed
Victoria and Albert Museum Ph 57–1983, 1 positive: image 17.6 × 22.7 cm, trimmed

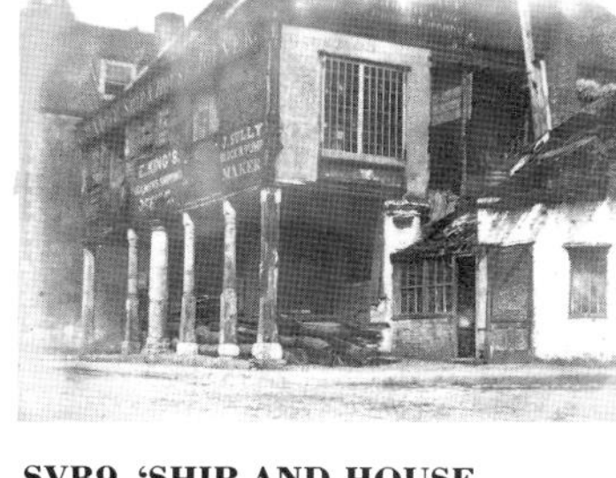

**SVB9 'SHIP AND HOUSE JOINER, J. SULLY BLOCK AND PUMP MAKER'**
VICTORIA AND ALBERT MUSEUM Ph 59–1983, 1 positive: image 21.5 × 16 cm, trimmed

**SVB10 Horse and carriage**
VICTORIA AND ALBERT MUSEUM Ph 98–1983, 1 positive: image 22.4 × 18 cm, trimmed

**SVB11 Shops and residences, sign YORK HAMS**
VICTORIA AND ALBERT MUSEUM Ph 61–1983, 1 positive: image 22.9 × 18.4 cm, trimmed

**SVB12 Sloping street with railing**
VICTORIA AND ALBERT MUSEUM Ph 63–1983, 1 positive: image 17.6 × 22.3 cm, trimmed

**SVB13 Residences**
VICTORIA AND ALBERT MUSEUM Ph 64–1983, 1 positive: image 18.6 × 22.4 cm, trimmed

**SVB14 Residences**
VICTORIA AND ALBERT MUSEUM Ph 108–1983, 1 positive: image 23 × 18 cm; trimmed, faint

## *Dublin*
## (SVI)

**SVI 1 City Hall, Dublin**
SCIENCE MUSEUM, negative 18 × 16.1 cm

**SVI 2 Trinity College, Old Library**
SCIENCE MUSEUM, negative 16.4 × 21.1 cm, verso in ink '549'

**SVI 3 Group outside Trinity College**
SCIENCE MUSEUM, 1 positive: sheet 16 × 20.9 cm; image 15.5 × 20.2 cm; negative 15.5 × 20.2 cm, verso in ink '550'

**SVI 4 Row of buildings Trinity College**
SCIENCE MUSEUM, negative 16.3 × 21.2 cm, waxed

**SVI 5 Trinity College**
SCIENCE MUSEUM, negative 18.7 × 16.3 cm

**SVI 6 Two storey house**
SCIENCE MUSEUM, negative 15.6 × 21.2 cm

**SVI 7 Large building with scaffolding**
SCIENCE MUSEUM, negative 15.6 × 20.6 cm

**SVI 8 Equestrian statue of William III, outside Bank of Ireland**
SCIENCE MUSEUM, 2 positives: sheet 10.9 × 18.5 cm; image 10 × 7.3 cm; negative 10 × 7.3 cm; 1 positive: sheet 8.7 × 10.5 cm; image 9.1 × 7.3 cm

**SVI 9 Merrion Square, West Dublin**
SCIENCE MUSEUM, 25 positives: sheet 12.3 × 18.2 cm; image 9.8 × 17.4 cm; negative 9.8 × 17.4 cm

**SVI 10 Street scene**
SCIENCE MUSEUM, negative 16.9 × 21.7 cm, inked sky

**SVI 11 Street scene**
SCIENCE MUSEUM, negative 16.5 × 21.5 cm

**SVI 12 Two gentlemen in front of building**
SCIENCE MUSEUM, negative 14.8 × 20.9 cm, waxed

## *Belgium*
## (SVBU)

**SVBU1 Market place, signs PHARMACIE . . . MORIEAL**
VICTORIA AND ALBERT MUSEUM Ph 100–1983, 1 positive: image 22.5 × 17.8 cm, trimmed

**SVBU2 '23 Rue de . . . '**
VICTORIA AND ALBERT MUSEUM Ph 102–1983, 1 positive: image 17.9 × 22 cm, trimmed

**SVBU3 'Rue des Rienn, Bruge' inscribed on negative**
VICTORIA AND ALBERT MUSEUM Ph 105–1983, 1 positive: image 17.8 × 22.8 cm, trimmed

**SVBU4 Houses bordering canal**
VICTORIA AND ALBERT MUSEUM Ph 106–1983, 1 positive: image 18.4 × 23.4 cm, trimmed

**SVBU5 Houses bordering canal (same location as SVBU4)**
VICTORIA AND ALBERT MUSEUM Ph 111–1983, 1 positive: image 22 × 18.5 cm, trimmed

**SVBU6 Shops and residences, sign LEGRAND BOUCHER**
VICTORIA AND ALBERT MUSEUM Ph 109–1983, 1 positive: image 22.4 × 17.5 cm, trimmed

**SVBU7 Square, sign VANDEN BOTTIER**
VICTORIA AND ALBERT MUSEUM Ph 114–1983, 1 positive: image 21.3 × 17 cm, trimmed

**SVBU8 Architectural sculpture on ornate buildings**
VICTORIA AND ALBERT MUSEUM Ph 115–1983, 1 positive: image 18.5 × 22.7 cm, trimmed

**SVBU9 Houses bordering canal**
VICTORIA AND ALBERT MUSEUM Ph 117–1983, 1 positive: image 18.1 × 23.1 cm, trimmed

**SVBU10 Street through arch in building**
VICTORIA AND ALBERT MUSEUM Ph 125–1983, 1 positive: image 10.7 × 18.5 cm, trimmed

**SVBU11 Antwerp**
HARRISON D HORBLIT COLLECTION, 1 positive: image 12.5 × 17.5 cm, trimmed, corners clipped

**SVBU12 'Maison des Baltiens (?), Ghent'**
HARRISON D HORBLIT COLLECTION, 1 positive: image 20.1 × 15.6 cm, trimmed

## *Florence* (SVF)

**SVF1 '484. Ponte Ste. Trieste, Florence'**
SCIENCE MUSEUM, 1 positive: sheet 22.8 × 18.9 cm; image 21.7 × 16.9 cm

**SVF2 '37. Piazza Granduca. Florence'**
SCIENCE MUSEUM, 2 positives: sheet 22.5 × 18.5 cm; image 21.5 × 16.8 cm; negative 21.2 × 16.5 cm, trimmed after printing

**SVF3 '85. . . . ? Arno, Florence'**
SCIENCE MUSEUM, 1 positive: sheet 23.1 × 18.7; image 22.5 × 16.7 cm

**SVF4 'Campanile . . .'**
SCIENCE MUSEUM, negative 16.4 × 21.2 cm, trimmed

**SVF5 Clock tower**
SCIENCE MUSEUM, negative 16.4 × 21.2 cm, trimmed

**SVF6 Campanile and temple**
SCIENCE MUSEUM, negative 20.3 × 16.3 cm; trimmed, inked sky, tabbed

**SVF7 Bridge**
LACOCK ABBEY COLLECTION LA 255, 1 positive: sheet 25 × 19.8 cm; image 21.3 × 16.8 cm

**SVF8 Square**
SCIENCE MUSEUM, negative 21.2 × 17.6, trimmed, waxed

## *Bologna* (SVBO)

**SVBO1 '93 Piazza del Gigante. Bologna.'**
SCIENCE MUSEUM, negative 18.6 × 22.5 cm

## *Rome* (SVR)

**SVR1 '26. Rome.' inscribed verso**
SCIENCE MUSEUM, 1 positive: sheet 11.6 × 9.8 cm; image 11.2 × 9.3 cm; negative 11.2 × 9.3 cm

**SVR2 '64. Ponte St. Angelo, Rome.' inscribed on negative**
SCIENCE MUSEUM, 1 positive: sheet 22.7 × 18.5 cm; image 22 × 16.8 cm; negative 22.6 × 16.6 cm; trimmed after printing, inked

**SVR3 Bridge, St Angelo**
SCIENCE MUSEUM, negative 21.2 × 15.9 cm; trimmed, waxed

**SVR4 '69. Near the Ponte St. Angelo, Rome.' inscribed on negative**
SCIENCE MUSEUM, 2 positives: sheet 23.5 × 18.5 cm; image 21.8 × 17.4 cm; negative 21.5 × 16.8 cm; trimmed, inked

## *Naples* (SVN)

**SVN1 Mapaniello's Market Place, Naples**
LACOCK ABBEY COLLECTION
LA 648, 1 positive: sheet 22.8 × 18.7 cm; image 20.6 × 16.7 cm
Science Museum, negative 20. 4 × 16.6 cm; trimmed, tabs
Division of Photographic History, Smithsonian Institution 67.172.4, sheet 22.7 × 18.6 cm; image 20.4 × 16.6 cm
Harrison D Horblit Collection, 1 positive: image 20.2 × 16.2 cm; trimmed, faint image, Talbot patent stamp verso

**SVN2 '36. Near the Mole, Naples.'**
SCIENCE MUSEUM, negative 20.9 × 16.8 cm, trimmed, waxed

## *France* (SVFR)

**SVFR1 Messagerie (coach office), Troyes**
HARRISON D HORBLIT COLLECTION, 1 positive: sheet 23.1 × 19.1 cm; image 21.5 × 18 cm, bad condition

## *Malta* (SVM)

**SVM1 '26. Piazza Vittoriosa.' listed in Small Talbotypes**
SCIENCE MUSEUM, 1 positive: sheet 10.9 × 9.2 cm; image 10.4 × 8.3 cm; negative 9.6 × 7.6 cm, trimmed after printing

**SVM2 'New church at Malta' inscribed**
SCIENCE MUSEUM, negative 22.4 × 18.5 cm, faint image

**SVM3 'Lookout tower Valetta, Malta'**
SCIENCE MUSEUM, negative 22.4 × 18.4 cm

**SVM4 'View in the late Mr. Frere's garden, Valetta'**
SCIENCE MUSEUM, negative 21.2 × 16.8 cm, trimmed, waxed

**SVM5 'Part of Governor's Palace, Valetta'**
SCIENCE MUSEUM, negative 16.8 × 21.2 cm, trimmed

**SVM6 Street Scene Valetta**
HANS P KRAUS JR COLLECTION, *Sun Pictures*, Catalogue IV, 21/22; 1 positive: 18.8 × 23.5 cm; image 15 × 21 cm, inscribed '65' in pencil verso; negative 15 × 21 cm, inscribed '28' and '65' verso

**SVM7 'Strada Ste. Lucia, Valetta'**
SCIENCE MUSEUM, 1 positive: sheet 18.6 × 22.7 cm; image 17.8 × 21.7 cm; negative 16.5 × 21.5 cm, trimmed after printing

**SVM8 Buildings fronting harbour**
SCIENCE MUSEUM, negative 16.5 × 21.2, trimmed

**SVM9 Buildings fronting harbour**
SCIENCE MUSEUM, negative 15.3 × 20.4 cm, trimmed

**SVM10 Buildings fronting harbour**
SCIENCE MUSEUM, negative 8.1 × 9.9 cm, trimmed

**SVM11 'On the Marina, Valetta'**
SCIENCE MUSEUM, negative 20.7 × 16.7 cm; bad condition, faint

**SVM12 '17. Strade Moline a Vente.' listed in Small Talbotypes**
SCIENCE MUSEUM, 1 positive: sheet 11.5 × 9.5 cm; image 8.7 × 9.9 cm; negative 8 × 8.7 cm, trimmed after printing

**SVM13 '39 Strade Veseovo. (bad paper)' listed in Small Talbotypes**
SCIENCE MUSEUM, 2 positives: sheet 8.8 × 11.3 cm; image 5.6 × 10.9 cm

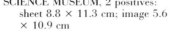

**SVM14 '33 Strade Marse Muscetto (bad paper)' listed in Small Talbotypes**
SCIENCE MUSEUM, 2 positives: sheet 11.2 × 9.6 cm; image 11 × 8.1 cm, trimmed; negative 8.7 × 7.9 cm; trimmed after printing, waxed

**SVM15 '16 Strade Marse Muscetto' listed in Small Talbotypes**
SCIENCE MUSEUM, 1 positive: sheet 11.5 × 9.1 cm, image 10.6 × 8.4 cm; negative 9.7 × 7.9 cm, trimmed after printing

**SVM16 'Strade Marse Muscetto' (same view as SV53)**
SCIENCE MUSEUM, negative 20.5 × 16.7 cm, trimmed

**SVM17 '10 Strade Marse Muscetto' listed in Small Talbotypes**
SCIENCE MUSEUM, 1 positive: sheet 11.4 × 9.3 cm, image 10.7 × 8.6 cm, trimmed; negative 9.7 × 7.9 cm, trimmed after printing

**SVM18 '12 Strade Marse Muscetto' listed in Small Talbotypes**
SCIENCE MUSEUM, 1 positive: sheet 9.5 × 11.4 cm; image 8.6 × 10.7 cm, trimmed; negative 7.9 × 10.1 cm, trimmed

**SVM19 Piazza Vittoriosa**
LACOCK ABBEY COLLECTION LA 2022 NB1, 1 positive: 20.9 × 15.3 cm, trimmed
Science Museum, negative 20.7 × 15.9 cm

**SVM20 '2. In Vittoriosa' listed in Small Talbotypes**
SCIENCE MUSEUM, 2 positives: sheet 9.1 × 11.6 cm; image 8.5 × 10.7 cm; negative 7.7 × 9.9 cm, trimmed after printing

**SVM21 '22. New Victualling Office.' Vittoriosa, listed in Small Talbotypes**

SCIENCE MUSEUM, 2 positives: sheet 11.3 × 9.4 cm; image 10.4 × 8.6 cm; negative 9.6 × 8 cm, trimmed after printing

**SVM22 '30. Piazza Regina.' listed in Small Talbotypes**
SCIENCE MUSEUM, 2 positives: sheet 11.3 × 9.5 cm; image 10.5 × 8.3 cm, trimmed; negative 10 × 8.2 cm, trimmed after printing

**SVM23 Piazza Regina**
SCIENCE MUSEUM, 1 positive: sheet 11.5 × 9.3 cm; image 9.7 × 7.9 cm; negative 9.7 × 7.9 cm

**SVM24 '34. Windmill.' listed in Small Talbotypes**
SCIENCE MUSEUM, 1 positive: sheet 11.6 × 9.7 cm; image 11 × 8.6 cm; negative 10.5 × 8.3 cm, trimmed after printing; very faint image

**SVM25 '36. Part of do. [ditto] Windmill.' listed in Small Talbotypes**

SCIENCE MUSEUM, 1 positive: sheet 11.7 × 9.8 cm; image 11.2 × 8.5 cm; negative 10.5 × 8.1 cm, trimmed after printing

**SVM26 Windmill**
SCIENCE MUSEUM, 2 positives: sheet 11.5 × 9.5 cm; image 10.8 × 8.6 cm; negative 18.8 × 8.6 cm, clipped corners

**SVM27 Street with windmill**
SCIENCE MUSEUM, negative 20 × 15.7 cm, trimmed

**SVM28 '20. Window.' listed in Small Talbotypes**
SCIENCE MUSEUM, 2 positives: sheet 9.2 × 11.1 cm; image 8.4 × 10.1 cm; negative 7.8 × 9.7 cm, trimmed after printing

**SVM29 Twin bell towers**

SCIENCE MUSEUM, negative 15.8 × 20.5 cm, trimmed

**SVM30 Twin bell towers**
SCIENCE MUSEUM, negative 15.4 × 20.9 cm; trimmed, waxed

**SVM31 Clock and bell tower**
SCIENCE MUSEUM, negative 15.5 × 21 cm; trimmed, waxed

**SVM32 Clock tower**
SCIENCE MUSEUM, negative 22.6 × 17.3 cm; waxed, inked

**SVM33 Square**
SCIENCE MUSEUM, negative 20.5 × 15.7 cm, trimmed

**SVM34 Six-columned facade**
SCIENCE MUSEUM, negative 22.5 × 17.5 cm; waxed, inked

**SVM35 Four-columned facade 'Vittoria Regina MDCCCXLII'**
SCIENCE MUSEUM, negative 10.6 × 8.5 cm, trimmed

**SVM36 Shops with awnings**
SCIENCE MUSEUM, 2 positives: sheet 10.3 × 8.2 cm; image 9.3 × 7.9 cm; negative 9.3 × 7.9 cm, trimmed

**SVM37 Shops with awnings**
SCIENCE MUSEUM, 1 positive: sheet 9.2 × 11.7; image 8.7 × 10.2 cm, very faint image; negative 8.7 × 10.2 cm

**SVM38 Old Bakery Street, Valetta**
SCIENCE MUSEUM, 5 positives: sheet 19.8 × 20.5 cm; image 15.4 × 20.4 cm
Lacock Abbey Collection LA 332/ LA 2015 NB1, 1 positive: sheet 20 × 20.5 cm; image 15.4 × 20.4 cm; 1 positive: image 14.5 × 19.9 cm, trimmed

**SVM39 Residences with balconies**
SCIENCE MUSEUM, negative 23.5 × 18.4 cm; waxed, inked

**SVM40 Residences with balconies**
SCIENCE MUSEUM, negative 15.4 × 21.1 cm; trimmed, inked

**SVM41 Residences with balconies**
SCIENCE MUSEUM, negative 16.5 × 23 cm, trimmed

**SVM42 Residences with balconies**
SCIENCE MUSEUM, negative 8 × 10 cm, trimmed

**SVM43 Residences with balconies**
SCIENCE MUSEUM, negative 20.4 × 15.8 cm, trimmed

**SVM44 Residences with balconies**
SCIENCE MUSEUM, negative 18.2 × 14.7 cm; trimmed, inked

**SVM45 Square with columned building**
SCIENCE MUSEUM, 1 positive: sheet 12.3 × 9.4 cm; image 11 × 8.5 cm

**SVM46 Square**
SCIENCE MUSEUM, 1 positive: sheet 12.1 × 9.2 cm; image 10.9 × 8.4 cm; negative 10.9 × 8.4, waxed

**SVM47 Formal building on square**
SCIENCE MUSEUM, 2 positives: sheet 10.7 × 9.6 cm; image 9.6 × 8.3 cm; negative 9.6 × 8.3 cm, trimmed, waxed

**SVM48 Market place (Italy?)**
SCIENCE MUSEUM, 2 positives: sheet 19.7 × 24.8 cm; image 16.4 × 21.4 cm
Lacock Abbey Collection LA 647, 1 positive: sheet 19.7 × 24.8 cm; image 16.4 × 21.4 cm

**SVM49 '39 Valetta Malta' inscribed on negative**
LACOCK ABBEY COLLECTION LA 345, 1 positive: sheet 22.6 × 18.6 cm; image 21.5 × 15.8 cm

Harrison D Horblit Collection, 1 positive: image 19.9 × 15.1 cm, trimmed

**SVM50 House with palm tree**
SCIENCE MUSEUM, negative 22.4 × 16.8 cm, inked

**SVM51 Bell cupola**
SCIENCE MUSEUM, negative 7.7 × 9.5 cm, trimmed

**SVM52 Clock tower**
SCIENCE MUSEUM, negative 10 × 8 cm

**SVM53 Lion fountain, inscribed, 'Square at Florina, Malta'**
SCIENCE MUSEUM, 1 positive: sheet 22.7 × 18.5 cm; image 21.7 × 17.7 cm; negative 21.5 × 16.6 cm, trimmed after printing
Lacock Abbey Collection 2017 NB1, 1 positive: image 21 × 15.7 cm, trimmed

**SVM54 Ornate building with balcony and niche**
SCIENCE MUSEUM, 1 positive: sheet 18.7 × 22.6 cm; image 15.7 × 20.7 cm, trimmed
Lacock Abbey Collection LA 2025 NB1, 1 positive: image 15.7 × 20.7 cm, trimmed

**SVM55 Ornate building with balcony and niche**
SCIENCE MUSEUM, 4 positives: sheet 9.3 × 11.3 cm; image 8.4 × 10.5 cm; negative 8.4 × 10.5 cm, trimmed

**SVM56 Ornate building with balcony and niche (third view)**
HARRISON D HORBLIT COLLECTION, 1 positive: image 15.4 × 20.9 cm, trimmed

**SVM57 '16 Ancient carriages of the Grand Masters, Valetta'**
LACOCK ABBEY COLLECTION LA 2023 NB1, 1 positive: image 20 × 15.4 cm, trimmed
Science Museum, negative 21.2 × 16.8 cm, trimmed

**SVM58 '17 Ancient Carriage of the Grand Master, Valetta'**
HANS P KRAUS JR COLLECTION, *Sun Pictures*, Catalogue IV, 28, negative: 22.5 × 18.6 cm; image 21.7 × 16.7 cm

**SVM59 'A View in the Island of Malta'**
THE ROBERT O DOUGAN COLLECTION, The Art Museum, Princeton University, 1 positive: 15.4 × 20.2 cm, trimmed

## ANTIQUITIES
### *Pompeii*
### (AP)

**AP1 '21. House of Tragic Poet Pompeii' inscribed verso; seated figure, probably CRM Talbot**
SCIENCE MUSEUM, 3 positives: sheet 11.3 × 9.6 cm; image 11.2 × 9.2 cm; negative 11.2 × 9.2 cm

**AP2 'House of the tragic poet' inscribed verso, with seated figure**
SCIENCE MUSEUM, 10 positives: sheet 11.4 × 9 cm; image 10.7 × 8.6 cm; negative 11.3 × 9.3, tabbed

**AP3 House of Sallust**
SCIENCE MUSEUM, 5 positives: sheet 24.9 × 19.6 cm; image 21.1 × 16.2 cm; negative 21.1 × 16.2 cm, trimmed, waxed
Science Museum, no 5 'House of Sallust, Ruins of Pompeii' in *Talbotypes or Sun Pictures* by Nicholaas Henneman, 1847
Royal Photographic Society 104, 1 positive: sheet 25.1 × 20 cm; image 21.2 × 16.5 cm
Division of Photographic History, Smithsonian Institution 67.172.31, 1 positive: sheet 24.9 × 19.8 cm; image 21.1 × 16.3 cm
Hans P Kraus Jr Collection, *Sun Pictures*, Catalogue IV, 24, 1 positive: sheet 24.7 × 19.7 cm; image 21.1 × 16.3 cm, inscribed 'I HW' in ink verso, intensified by Harold White
David Alan Brown Collection, 1 positive: image 21.1 × 16.3 cm, trimmed (see Hand-Coloured Calotypes H-C 1)
Robert Hershkowitz Ltd, 1 positive: sheet 24.5 × 19.5 cm; image 21.2 × 16.5 cm

**AP4 'No. 50 Street of Pompeii leading to Forum.' inscribed on positive**
SCIENCE MUSEUM, positive: sheet 22.9 × 18.6 cm; image 22.3 × 18.5 cm; also inscribed, in pencil in a different hand, 'Darkened the sky as far as the line. This copy is too weak a stronger one will bring out the mountains.' negative 21 × 16.5 cm; trimmed, inked sky

**AP5 Forum**
SCIENCE MUSEUM, negative 21.3 × 16.6 cm; trimmed, waxed

**AP6 Forum with standing figure**
SCIENCE MUSEUM, 1 positive: sheet 24.8 × 20.3 cm; image 21.1 × 16.3 cm; negative 21 × 16.7 cm

**AP7 Forum**
SCIENCE MUSEUM, negative 20.8 × 16.1 cm

**AP8 '18 Near view of arch. Forum, Pompeii' inscribed verso**
SCIENCE MUSEUM, 13 positives: sheet 11 × 9.3 cm; image 10.8 × 8.5 cm; negative 11.2 × 9.3 cm, tabbed

**AP9 'Arch leading to Forum, Pompeii' inscribed**
SCIENCE MUSEUM, 1 positive: sheet 11.4 × 8.9 cm; image 10.5 × 8.5 cm; negative 11.2 × 9.2 cm, tabbed

**AP10 '14. House of the Vestals Pompeii' inscribed verso**
SCIENCE MUSEUM, 4 positives: sheet 11.1 × 9.6 cm; image 10.4 × 8.7 cm; negative 11.2 × 9.3 cm, waxed

**AP11 '16 Flour Mill, Pompeii' inscribed on negative**
SCIENCE MUSEUM, 2 positives: sheet 11.6 × 9.3 cm; image 10.5 × 8.6 cm; negative 11.2 × 9.3 cm

**AP12 '13. In the Basilica, Pompeii' inscribed on negative**
SCIENCE MUSEUM, 6 positives: sheet 8.5 × 11.9 cm; image 8.1 × 10.5 cm; negative 9.3 × 11.2 cm

**AP13 '19 House of Castor and Pollux, Pompeii' inscribed**
SCIENCE MUSEUM, 7 positives: sheet 11.4 × 9.4 cm; image 10.8 × 8.6 cm; negative 11.2 × 9.3 cm

**AP14 'House lately excavated' inscribed on negative verso**
SCIENCE MUSEUM, 7 positives: sheet 11.6 × 10.3 cm; image 10.3 × 8.8 cm; negative 11.2 × 9.3 cm

**AP15 '11. Household altar' inscribed on negative verso**
SCIENCE MUSEUM, 1 positive: sheet 9.1 × 11.2 cm; image 8.6 × 10.7 cm; negative 9.3 × 11.2 cm, waxed

**AP16 'Temple of Venus. Pompeii' inscribed on negative**
SCIENCE MUSEUM, 2 positives: sheet 11.1 × 9.1 cm; image 10.5 × 8.5 cm; negative 11.2 × 9.3 cm, tabbed

**AP17 'Drinking table and wine cooler. Pompeii' inscribed on negative verso**
SCIENCE MUSEUM, 13 positives: sheet 12.5 × 9.8 cm; image 10.9 × 8.7 cm; negative 11.2 × 9.3 cm, waxed

**AP18 Drinking table and wine cooler**
SCIENCE MUSEUM, 1 positive: sheet 11.5 × 9.6 cm, image 10.9 × 8.6 cm; negative 10.1 × 7.9 cm

**AP19 Street of Pompeii with figures**
HARRISON D HORBLIT COLLECTION, 1 positive: image 21.5 × 16 cm, trimmed

**AP20 Temple of Diomedes**
HARRISON D HORBLIT COLLECTION, 1 positive: image 20.6 × 16.6 cm, trimmed

**AP21 Silversmith's Street**
HARRISON D HORBLIT COLLECTION, 1 positive: image 20.1 × 16.2 cm; trimmed, faint image

*Rome*
**(AR)**

**AR1 '72 Forum of Trajan (joins 73 at xx)' inscribed on negative verso**
SCIENCE MUSEUM, 1 positive: sheet 23.6 × 17.6 cm; image 21.8 × 16.8 cm; negative 21.8 × 16.8 cm, waxed
Hans P Kraus Jr Collection, 1 positive: sheet 23.1 × 18.4 cm; image 21.8 × 16.8 cm

**AR2 '73 Forum of Trajan (joins 72 at xx)' inscribed on negative verso**
SCIENCE MUSEUM, 7 positives: sheet 22.7 × 18.2 cm; image 21.9 × 16.7 cm; negative 22.5 × 18.5 cm, waxed

**AR3 View of the Forum**
SCIENCE MUSEUM, negative 16.4 × 21.3 cm; trimmed, tabbed

**AR4 View of Forum with horses and carts**
SCIENCE MUSEUM, negative 21.1 × 16.1 cm

**AR5 '70 Temple of Vesta and R . . . , Rome' inscribed**
SCIENCE MUSEUM, 5 positives: sheet 24.8 × 19.6 cm; image 21.6 × 16.2 cm; negative 21.6 × 16.8 cm; trimmed, tabbed, inked sky, brushwork on architecture
Royal Library of Copenhagen 1967 – 337/12, 1 positive: sheet 25.1 × 19.5 cm; image 21.6 × 16.3 cm

**AR6 'Arch of Titus, Colosseum' inscribed in Talbot album**
LACOCK ABBEY COLLECTION LA 2024 NB1, 1 positive: 21.3 × 16.3 cm, trimmed

**AR7 'Temple of Antoninus and Faustina, Rome, Rev. C. Jones 1846.' inscribed in Talbot album**
LACOCK ABBEY COLLECTION LA 2019 NB, 1 positive: 21.5 × 16.6 cm
Science Museum, 1 positive: 21.6 × 16.7 cm; negative 21.3 × 16.3 cm, trimmed
Science Museum No 6 in *Talbotypes or Sun Pictures* by Nicholaas Henneman, 1847

**AR8 '67. Colosseum Rome 2nd view' inscribed**
ROYAL LIBRARY OF COPENHAGEN 1967 337/10, 1 positive: sheet 24.9 × 19.6 cm; image 21.7 × 17.3 cm
Science Museum, (1401/73), 12 positives: 21.7 × 17.3 cm
Royal Photographic Society, 1 positive: 20.9 × 16.3 cm, trimmed
Division of Photographic History Smithsonian Institution 67.172.1, 1 positive: sheet 22.4 × 18.5 cm; image 21.7 × 17.3 cm
Hans P Kraus Jr Collection, *Sun Pictures*, Catalogue IV, 23,
1 positive: sheet 24.9 × 19.7 cm; image 22.4 × 18.6 cm

**AR9 '60. Colosseum Rome' inscribed**
SCIENCE MUSEUM, (1403/73) 5 positives: sheet 22.8 × 18.6 cm; image 21.6 × 16.7 cm; negative 20.9 × 16.3 cm; trimmed, waxed
Andre and Marie-Therese Jammes Collection, 1 positive: image 20.9 × 16.3 cm

## CASTLES AND MANOR HOUSES (CM)

*Wales*

**CM1 Swansea Castle**
SCIENCE MUSEUM, 9 positives: sheet 18.4 × 22.4 cm; image 16.3 × 20.7 cm; negative 16.3 × 20.7 cm, trimmed
Science Museum, No 11 in *Talbotypes or Sun Pictures* by Nicholaas Henneman, 1847
Royal Library, Copenhagen 1967 – 337/13, 1 positive: sheet 18.6 × 22.8 cm; image 16.3 × 20.7 cm
Lacock Abbey Collection LA 2041 NB1, inscribed in Talbot Album, 'Rev. C. Jones Swansea Castle'; 1 positive: image 16 × 19.8 cm, trimmed
Royal Photographic Society 54, 1 positive: sheet 16.6 × 25.3 cm; image 16.5 × 20.8 cm
Hans P Kraus Jr Collection, 1 positive: sheet 18.5 × 22.4 cm; image 16.8 × 20.7 cm

**CM2 Swansea Castle**
HARRISON D HORBLIT COLLECTION, 1 positive: image 19.3 × 15.6 cm; trimmed
Science Museum, negative 19.8 × 16.3 cm, trimmed

**CM3 Swansea Castle**
SCIENCE MUSEUM, negative 21 × 16.3 cm

**CM4 Cardiff Castle, '191' inscribed on print**
SCIENCE MUSEUM W 14, 5 positives: sheet 20 × 24.9 cm; image 16.8 × 22 cm

**CM5 Cardiff Castle, '193' inscribed verso**
SCIENCE MUSEUM, 1 positive: sheet 19.6 × 22.7 cm; image 17.2 × 21.8 cm

**CM6 Margam Castle, west front**
VICTORIA AND ALBERT MUSEUM Ph 74–1983, 1 positive: image 21.5 × 17.5 cm, trimmed

**CM7 Margam Castle lawn with group (see PG1)**
VICTORIA AND ALBERT MUSEUM Ph 72–1983, 1 positive: image 18.5 × 21.9 cm, trimmed

**CM8 Margam, two figures on lawn (possibly CRM Talbot seated, and son Theo) (see PG1)**
VICTORIA AND ALBERT MUSEUM Ph 73–1983, 1 positive: image 18.5 × 22 cm, trimmed

**CM9 Margam, east front, figure on lawn**
VICTORIA AND ALBERT MUSEUM Ph 71–1983, 1 positive: image 22.4 × 18.3 cm, trimmed

**CM10 Margam, south front with stables**
VICTORIA AND ALBERT MUSEUM Ph 69–1983, 1 positive: image 22.6 × 17.7 cm, trimmed

**CM11 Orangery at Margam Park**
VICTORIA AND ALBERT MUSEUM Ph 75–1983, 1 positive: image 23 × 18.5 cm, trimmed
Harrison D Horblit Collection 22, 1 positive: image 22.4 × 18.3 cm

**CM12 '"Inigo Jones" Summer House, Margam, Mr. and Mrs. C.R. Jones' inscribed on mount**
HARRISON D HORBLIT COLLECTION 23, 1 positive: image 17.9 × 22.2 cm, trimmed; attributed to CRJ

**CM13 Margam, southwest view with stables**
NATIONAL LIBRARY OF WALES, Daguerreotype: plate 20.5 × 15.4 cm; image 19.9 × 13.8 cm; verso inscribed 'March 9t, 1841 9h. 30m. A.M./ In the camera 26 min. Sun clear throughout./ Mercury 7 min. rising. 9 falling./ Calvert R. Jones'

**CM14 Heathfield Lodge, Swansea**
VICTORIA AND ALBERT MUSEUM Ph 128–1983, 1 positive: image 16.5 × 11 cm, trimmed

**CM15 Country House**
VICTORIA AND ALBERT MUSEUM Ph 86–1983, 1 positive: image 22.3 × 17.6 cm, trimmed

**CM16 Ruin**
ROYAL PHOTOGRAPHIC SOCIETY, 1 of 4 positives on single sheet 25 × 19.6 cm; image 8.7 × 11.5 cm

**CM17 Singleton Abbey**
ROYAL INSTITUTION OF SOUTH WALES 29, 2 positives: image 20.5 × 15.5 cm, trimmed
Division of Photographic History, Smithsonian Institution 67.172.39, 1 positive: sheet 23.8 × 19.5 cm; image 20.9 × 15.9 cm

## *England*

**CM18 Hampton Court with two figures**
SCIENCE MUSEUM, 2 positives: sheet 9.4 × 11.5 cm; image 8.4 × 10.5 cm; negative 8.4 × 10.5 cm; trimmed, corners clipped

**CM19 Hampton Court with figures**
SCIENCE MUSEUM, 1 positive: sheet 11.3 × 9.2 cm; image 10.2 × 8.5 cm; negative 10.2 × 8.5 cm; trimmed, corners clipped

**CM20 Hampton Court**
SCIENCE MUSEUM, 6 positives: sheet 9.2 × 11.8 cm; image 8.4 × 10.2 cm; negative 8.4 × 10.2 cm; trimmed, corners clipped

**CM21 Hampton Court**
SCIENCE MUSEUM, 1 positive: sheet 9.2 × 11.5 cm; image 8.3 × 10.5 cm; negative 8.3 × 10.5 cm; trimmed, corners clipped

**CM22 Hampton Court**
SCIENCE MUSEUM, 3 positives: sheet 11 × 8.7 cm; image 10 × 8 cm

**CM23 Hampton Court**
SCIENCE MUSEUM, 1 positive: sheet 9.1 × 10.9 cm; image 8.2 × 10.1 cm

## *Ireland*

**CM24 Dublin Castle**
SCIENCE MUSEUM, negative 20.4 × 16.5 cm

**CM25 Castle ruin**
SCIENCE MUSEUM, negative 13.8 × 20.8 cm; waxed, verso in ink '573'

**CM26 Castle**
SCIENCE MUSEUM, negative 15.3 × 18.5 cm, waxed

**CM27 Castle**
SCIENCE MUSEUM, negative 15.3 × 21.2 cm

**CM28 Powerscourt, County Wicklow**
SCIENCE MUSEUM, negative 12.2 × 18.7 cm, waxed

**CM29 Powerscourt**
SCIENCE MUSEUM, 2 positives: sheet 9.6 × 10.5 cm, image 9.4 × 7.4 cm; negative 9.4 × 7.4 cm

**CM30 Powerscourt**
SCIENCE MUSEUM, negative 15.5 × 21 cm

**CM31 Powerscourt**
SCIENCE MUSEUM, negative 6.6 × 9.4 cm, waxed

## CATHEDRALS AND CHURCHES (CC)

**CC1 '20 Cathedral Messina (joins 19 at xx)' inscribed verso**
ROYAL PHOTOGRAPHIC SOCIETY 53, 1 positive: sheet 18.5 × 22.5 cm; image 16.9 × 22.2 cm
Science Museum, negative 18.5 × 22.5 cm; inked sky, carts inked out
Royal Photographic Society 100, 1 positive: sheet 18.4 × 23 cm; image 16.8 × 22 cm, right edge trimmed; printed from N 39A before inking
Division of Photographic History, Smithsonian Institution 67.172.24, 1 positive: sheet 19.5 × 23.8 cm; image 16.8 × 21.8 cm

**CC2 'x 19 Cathedral. Messina (joins 20 at xx)', joiner to N 39A, inscribed verso**
SCIENCE MUSEUM, negative 18.5 × 22.5 cm, inked sky

**CC3 '21 part of Cathedral Messina' inscribed**
SCIENCE MUSEUM, negative 16.9 × 21.2 cm; trimmed, inked sky

**CC4 '23 Chiese Ste. Caterina', Messina, inscribed**
SCIENCE MUSEUM, negative 16.5 × 20.5 cm, trimmed

**CC5 Ste Maria della Scala**
SCIENCE MUSEUM, negative 20.9 × 17.3 cm

**CC6 West Side of Church of Ste Maria, Florence**
SCIENCE MUSEUM, negative 15.3 × 18.7 cm, trimmed

**CC7 View of St Peter's**
SCIENCE MUSEUM, 2 positives: image 20.6 × 16 cm, trimmed; negative 20.8 × 16.4 cm; trimmed, waxed

**CC8 West side of Church of Ste della Majore, Rome**
SCIENCE MUSEUM, negative 21.1 × 16.7 cm; trimmed after printing, waxed

**CC9 '63 View of Vatican, Rome'**
SCIENCE MUSEUM, 1 positive: sheet 22.8 × 18.5 cm; image 21.5 × 16.8 cm; negative 21.1 × 16.2 cm; trimmed after printing, waxed

**CC10 '100 Duomo. Milan (joins 99 at 00)' inscribed**
SCIENCE MUSEUM, 1 positive: sheet 19.6 × 24 cm; image 16.6 × 21.5 cm

**CC11 Village church**
VICTORIA AND ALBERT MUSEUM Ph 124–1983, 1 positive: image 16.5 × 21.2 cm, trimmed

**CC12 Cathedral with rows of tents**
VICTORIA AND ALBERT MUSEUM Ph 107–1983, 1 positive: image 21.4 × 17.6 cm, trimmed

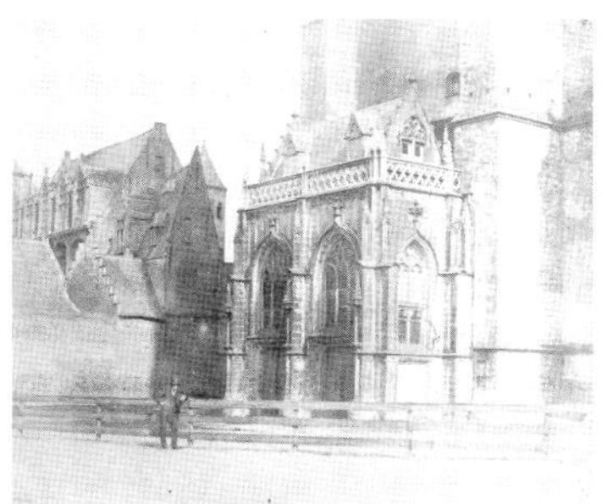

**CC13 Temporary rail fence with figure**
VICTORIA AND ALBERT MUSEUM Ph 112–1983, 1 positive: image 22.6 × 18.2 cm, trimmed

**CC14 Cathedral with clock tower**
VICTORIA AND ALBERT MUSEUM Ph 123–1983, 1 positive: image 17.5 × 22 cm, trimmed

**CC15 St Paul's Anglican Cathedral, Malta**
SCIENCE MUSEUM, negative 15.6 × 21 cm

**CC16 Maltese church**
SCIENCE MUSEUM, negative 10 × 8.3 cm, trimmed

**CC17 York Minster**
LACOCK ABBEY COLLECTION
LA 779, 1 positive: sheet 18.9 × 22.9 cm; image 18.4 × 22.5 cm

**CC18 York Minster**
SCIENCE MUSEUM, negative 10.2 × 9 cm, trimmed; attributed to CRJ

**CC19 York Minster**
SCIENCE MUSEUM, 1 positive: sheet 11.4 × 9.2 cm; image 11.2 × 8.9 cm; negative 11.2 × 8.9 cm; attributed to CRJ

**CC20 York Minster**
SCIENCE MUSEUM, 1 positive: sheet 11.4 × 9.4 cm; image 11.3 × 8.7 cm; negative 11.4 × 9 cm; attributed to CRJ

**CC21 York Minster**
SCIENCE MUSEUM, 1 positive: image 9.2 × 8.3 cm, trimmed; negative 9.2 × 8.4 cm; trimmed, waxed; attributed to CRJ

**CC22 Façade of south transept, York Minster**
SCIENCE MUSEUM, 9 positives: sheet 10 × 10.3 cm; image 8.4 × 9.6 cm; negative 8.4 × 9.6 cm; trimmed, waxed; attributed to CRJ

**CC23 Street leading to York Minster**
SCIENCE MUSEUM, 1 positive: sheet 9.7 × 11.5 cm; image 9.5 × 8 cm; negative 9.5 × 8 cm; trimmed, waxed; attributed to CRJ

**CC24 St George's Church, Dublin**
HANS P KRAUS JR COLLECTION, *Sun Pictures*, Catalogue IV, 29; 1 positive: sheet 19.2 × 23.5 cm; image 16.2 × 20.1 cm, 1 positive: sheet 18.8 × 22.7 cm; image 16.1 × 20 cm, inscribed 'IHW' in ink verso, intensified by Harold White; negative image of cathedral and Roman forum verso
Division of Photographic History, Smithsonian Institution 67.172.41, 1 positive: sheet 19.6 × 24 cm; image 16.3 × 20.3 cm, watermark J Whatman

**CC25 Canterbury, Pilgrim's Porch**
HANS P KRAUS JR COLLECTION, 1 positive: sheet 23.9 × 19.5 cm; image 22.1 × 17.1 cm

**CC26 Church on Piazza**
HARRISON D HORBLIT COLLECTION, 1 positive: sheet 23.4 × 19.4 cm; image 20.4 × 15.1 cm

**CC27 Maltese church**
HARRISON D HORBLIT COLLECTION, 1 positive: sheet 22.6 × 18.7 cm; image 20.4 × 16.1 cm, faint image

**CC28 Black Church, Dublin**
SCIENCE MUSEUM, negative 20.7 × 16.2 cm

**CC29 Protestant Cathedral, Dublin**
SCIENCE MUSEUM, negative 16.1 × 20.1 cm

**CC30 Church, Dublin**
SCIENCE MUSEUM, negative 19 × 16.1 cm, waxed

## PARKS AND STATUARY (PS)

**PS1 Dolphin fountain**
LACOCK ABBEY COLLECTION LA 827, 1 positive: sheet 22.9 × 18 cm; image 22 × 16.9 cm, watermark Whatman 1846
Science Museum, 1 positive: sheet 22.6 × 18.6 cm; image 22 × 16.9 cm
Division of Photographic History, Smithsonian Institution 3864.21, negative 22 × 17.5 cm

**PS2 Dolphin fountain**
VICTORIA AND ALBERT MUSEUM Ph 32–1983, 1 positive: image 22 × 17.7 cm, trimmed

**PS3 Yucca and decorative urn**
SCIENCE MUSEUM, 1 positive: sheet 18.2 × 23 cm; image 16.7 × 22.2 cm

**PS4 Cactus, inscribed 'No. 2 Cactus opuntia. Indian figs Malta'**
SCIENCE MUSEUM, 1 positive: sheet 10.1 × 9 cm; image 9.9 × 8 cm, trimmed; negative 9.9 × 8 cm, trimmed

**PS5 Cactus (opuntia)**
SCIENCE MUSEUM, negative 10.2 × 8.1 cm, trimmed

**PS6 Urn and balustrade**
VICTORIA AND ALBERT MUSEUM Ph 93–1983, 1 positive: image 8.5 × 10.6 cm, trimmed

**PS7A '81. Rape of the Sabines (1st view) Florence'**
ROYAL PHOTOGRAPHIC SOCIETY 99, 1 positive: sheet 18.2 × 23.3 cm; image 17.6 × 22.2 cm

**PS7 '82. Rape of the Sabines (2nd view) Florence'**
SCIENCE MUSEUM, 1 positive: sheet 18.6 × 22.7 cm; image 17.2 × 21.3 cm; ghost figures on wall, inked around statue

**PS8 Statue in Florence**
SCIENCE MUSEUM, 2 positives: sheet 24.7 × 19.5 cm; image 16.6 × 21.1 cm, trimmed; negative 16.6 × 21.1 cm, trimmed

**PS9 '38. Piazza Vittoriosa', listed in Small Talbotypes**
SCIENCE MUSEUM, 2 positives: sheet 9.7 × 11.2 cm; image 8.6 × 10.8 cm; negative 8.2 × 9.7 cm, trimmed after printing

**PS10 '47. Piazza Vittoriosa', listed in Small Talbotypes**
SCIENCE MUSEUM, 1 positive: sheet 9.2 × 10.8 cm; image 8.8 × 9.4 cm; negative 7.6 × 8.8 cm, trimmed after printing

**PS11 '39. Celebrated obelisk, Naples' inscribed**
SCIENCE MUSEUM, 8 positives: sheet 19.6 × 24.9 cm; image 16.5 × 21.2 cm; negative 16.5 × 21.2 cm; trimmed, waxed

**PS12 '74. Horses on Monte Cavellon, Rome', inscribed**
SCIENCE MUSEUM, 1 positive: sheet 22.5 × 18.5 cm; image 21.9 × 16.9 cm, very faint; negative 21.1 × 16.3 cm; trimmed after printing, waxed

**PS13 '62. The Obelisk of Palazzo Chigi . . . Rome', inscribed**
SCIENCE MUSEUM, 1 positive: sheet 18.2 × 22.8 cm; image 16.8 × 21.6 cm
The J Paul Getty Museum 85.XM.150.8, 1 positive: sheet 18.6 × 22.8 cm; image 16.8 × 21.6 cm

**PS14 '76. Statue of M. Aurelius. Capitol. Rome', inscribed**
SCIENCE MUSEUM, 1 positive: sheet 22.5 × 18.7 cm; image 21.8 × 16.8 cm

**PS15 High view of Villa Reale, inscribed in Talbot album 'Naples'**
LACOCK ABBEY COLLECTION LA 2021 NB1/LA 773, 2 positives: sheet 23.7 × 19.5 cm; image 20.8 × 15.6 cm; watermark J Whatman 1846
Science Museum, negative 20.8 × 15.6 cm; trimmed, waxed

**PS16 Villa Reale**
LACOCK ABBEY COLLECTION LA 772, 1 positive: sheet 22.5 × 18.5 cm; image 20.3 × 15.8 cm; watermark, lamb logo
Science Museum, negative 20.3 × 15.8 cm

**PS17 'Villa Reale Naples May 30, 1846 5 minutes good sun no diaphragm' inscribed; statue with girl**
SCIENCE MUSEUM, 1 positive: sheet 22.3 × 18.5 cm; image 21.3 × 15.8 cm

**PS18 'Statue of the fawn bound Naples May 31, 1846 7 minutes hot sun' inscribed**
SCIENCE MUSEUM, 1 positive: sheet 22.2 × 18.6 cm; image 20.9 × 15.7 cm

**PS19 Monument, Dublin**
SCIENCE MUSEUM, negative 16.6 × 16.6 cm

## PORTRAITS
### *Environmental*
### (PE)

**PE1 '12. Truck and man sitting down' from list sent to London, 26 March 1847**
SCIENCE MUSEUM, negative 16.5 × 21.3 cm; trimmed, waxed
Science Museum, 12. Dove Cote, Singleton in *Talbotypes or Sun Pictures* by Nicholaas Henneman, 1847
Division of Photographic History, Smithsonian Institution, 167.172.30, sheet 20.2 × 25.3 cm; image 16.5 × 21.9 cm

**PE2 Man in top hat, Malta**
HARRISON D HORBLIT COLLECTION, 1 positive: image 14.8 × 19 cm, trimmed

**PE3 Harbour at low tide with figures**
LACOCK ABBEY COLLECTION LA 502, 1 positive: 20.2 × 15.2 cm, trimmed

**PE4 Longboat with two figures**
LACOCK ABBEY COLLECTION LA 513, 2 positives: sheet 23.4 × 18.3 cm, image 22 × 17 cm; watermark J Whatman 1846

**PE5 Beach with figures**
LACOCK ABBEY COLLECTION LA 654, 8 positives: sheet 24.9 × 20 cm; image 20.8 × 14.9 cm Science Museum, negative 20.8 × 14.9 cm; trimmed, waxed

**PE6 Seated woman on palm trunk**
SCIENCE MUSEUM, 1 positive: sheet 18.3 × 22.9 cm; image 16.6 × 21.1 cm; negative 16.6 × 21.1 cm; trimmed, waxed
Hans P Kraus Jr Collection, 1 positive: sheet 18.3 × 22.9 cm; image 16.6 × 21.1 cm

**PE7 '5. St. Paul's Bay Malta (joins No. 6 at xx)' inscribed**
SCIENCE MUSEUM, 1 positive: sheet 22.8 × 18.8 cm; image 21.8 × 16.7 cm; negative 21.8 × 16.7 cm, inked sky

Hans P Kraus Collection, 1 positive: sheet 18.3 × 22.4 cm; image 16.7 × 21.7 cm

**PE8 St Paul's Bay with figures on shore**
SCIENCE MUSEUM, 1 positive: sheet 23.8 × 19.2 cm; image 22.5 × 18.5 cm; negative 21.5 × 16.7 cm; trimmed, waxed

**PE9 Public building with figure on steps**
SCIENCE MUSEUM, negative 21.2 × 15.9 cm, trimmed

**PE10 Top-hatted man in road**
VICTORIA AND ALBERT MUSEUM Ph 88–1983, 1 positive: 21.5 × 17.1 cm, trimmed

**PE11 Seascape with figure (Caswell Bay?)**
VICTORIA AND ALBERT MUSEUM Ph 89, 1 positive: image 10.2 × 8.8 cm

**PE12 Reclining figure**
VICTORIA AND ALBERT MUSEUM Ph 82, 1 positive: image 17.3 × 22.1 cm, ink brushwork

**PE13 Man beside arch, Bristol**
VICTORIA AND ALBERT MUSEUM Ph 40–1983, 1 positive: image 18 × 21.2 cm, trimmed

**PE14 Woman beside arch, Bristol**
VICTORIA AND ALBERT MUSEUM Ph 45–1983, 1 positive: image 18 × 21.3 cm, trimmed

**PE15 Man beside arch, Bristol**
VICTORIA AND ALBERT MUSEUM Ph 49–1983, 1 positive: image 17.2 × 21.8 cm, trimmed

**PE16 Man beside lamp post, Bristol**
VICTORIA AND ALBERT MUSEUM Ph 37–1983, 1 positive: image 22.5 × 17.6 cm, trimmed

**PE17 Man beside ship in dry dock**
VICTORIA AND ALBERT MUSEUM Ph 56–1983, 1 positive: image 21.5 × 17.8 cm, trimmed

**PE18 Man seated on plank in shipyard**
VICTORIA AND ALBERT MUSEUM Ph 50–1983, 1 positive: image 22.1 × 17.8 cm, trimmed

**PE19 Women on deck of ship in dry dock**
VICTORIA AND ALBERT MUSEUM Ph 38–1983, 1 positive: image 22.6 × 18.9 cm, trimmed

**PE20 Man seated on steps**
VICTORIA AND ALBERT MUSEUM Ph 67–1983, 1 positive: image 21.2 × 16.5 cm, trimmed

**PE21 Two men on step**
VICTORIA AND ALBERT MUSEUM Ph 30–1983, 1 positive: image 20.5 × 15.7 cm, trimmed

**PE22 Man standing by fence**
VICTORIA AND ALBERT MUSEUM Ph 65–1983, 1 positive: image 18 × 21.7 cm, trimmed

**PE23 Man by ornate doorway, Venice**
VICTORIA AND ALBERT MUSEUM Ph 65–1983, 1 positive: image 16.6 × 21.5 cm, trimmed

**PE24 Man standing by Four Star Tavern, Bristol**
HARRISON D HORBLIT COLLECTION 21, 1 positive: image 17.5 × 22.5 cm, trimmed
Victoria and Albert Museum Ph 62–1983, 1 positive: image 17.8 × 22.5 cm, trimmed

**PE25 Two men by colonnade, Bath**
VICTORIA AND ALBERT MUSEUM Ph 35, 1 positive: image 22.2 × 18.9 cm, trimmed

**PE26 Man seated in front of Rheola House, Neath Valley**
VICTORIA AND ALBERT MUSEUM Ph 79–1983, 1 positive: image 20.7 × 17.6 cm, trimmed

**PE27 Group at Rheola House**
VICTORIA AND ALBERT MUSEUM Ph 80–1983, 1 positive: image 18 × 20.9 cm, trimmed

**PE28 Group in front of Rheola House**
VICTORIA AND ALBERT MUSEUM Ph 81–1983, 1 positive: image 23 × 18.3 cm, trimmed

**PE29 Group in front of manor house**
VICTORIA AND ALBERT MUSEUM Ph 84–1983, 1 positive: image 22.7 × 17.2 cm, trimmed; doubtful attribution

**PE30 Figure seated in front of manor house**
VICTORIA AND ALBERT MUSEUM Ph 85–1983, 1 positive: image 22.4 × 17.9 cm, trimmed; doubtful attribution

**PE31 Man in front of manor house (same setting as PG22)**
VICTORIA AND ALBERT MUSEUM Ph 91–1983, 1 positive: 21.5 × 16.4 cm, trimmed

**PE32 Two figures under ivy-covered tree**
VICTORIA AND ALBERT MUSEUM Ph 83–1983, 1 positive: image 18.6 × 23 cm, trimmed

**PE33 Group in Cloisters**
HARRISON D HORBLIT COLLECTION, 1 positive: sheet 18.8 × 22.8 cm; image 17.1 × 19.4 cm, watermark Whatman 1846

## *Group* (PG)

**PG1 C R M Talbot family and Mrs C R Jones posed before Margam Castle**
HARRISON D HORBLIT COLLECTION, positive joined: 18.6 × 22 cm (left joiner) 17.2 × 22 cm (right joiner)

**PG2 Man in coat and plaid waistcoat, and woman, possibly Ann Harriet Jones**
VICTORIA AND ALBERT MUSEUM Ph 77–1983, 1 positive: image 8.3 × 10.6 cm, trimmed

**PG3 Family group, possibly CRJ, Ann Harriet and Christina**
VICTORIA AND ALBERT MUSEUM Ph 33–1983 (c), 1 positive: image 8.6 × 9.8 cm, trimmed

**PG4 Family group in front of door, inscribed '29'**
ROYAL PHOTOGRAPHIC SOCIETY, 1 of 4 positives on single sheet 25 × 19.6 cm; image 10.5 × 8.6 cm

**PG5 Two figures by house wall**
VICTORIA AND ALBERT MUSEUM Ph 97–1983, 1 positive: image 21.4 × 15.3 cm, trimmed

**PG6 Man and woman by arch**
VICTORIA AND ALBERT MUSEUM Ph 95–1983, 1 positive: image 16.3 × 21.7 cm, trimmed

**PG7 Family group by arch**
VICTORIA AND ALBERT MUSEUM Ph 92–1983, 1 positive: image 16.9 × 22.1 cm, trimmed

**PG8 Family group**
VICTORIA AND ALBERT MUSEUM Ph 94–1983, 1 positive: image 11.1 × 8.7 cm, trimmed

**PG9 Family group, Malta**
SCIENCE MUSEUM, 3 positives: sheet 11.5 × 9.4 cm; image 10.6 × 8.5; negative 9.7 × 7.8 cm, trimmed

**PG10 Family group, Malta**
SCIENCE MUSEUM, 2 positives: sheet 11.2 × 9.2 cm; image 10.6 × 8.6 cm; negative 9.2 × 7.9 cm, trimmed

**PG11 '43. Dominican Friars.'**
SCIENCE MUSEUM, 2 positives: sheet 10.3 × 9 cm; image 9.8 × 8.3 cm; negative 9.8 × 8.3 cm; trimmed, part of background inked over

**PG12 '44. Capucin [*sic*] ditto.'**
SCIENCE MUSEUM, 2 positives: sheet 10.7 × 9.9 cm; image 10 × 8.3 cm; negative 10 × 8.3 cm; trimmed, part of background inked over

**PG13 Group of Greeks**
HARRISON D HORBLIT COLLECTION, 1 positive: sheet 22.9 × 18.3 cm; image 21.7 × 16.6 cm

**PG14 '40. Group of Greek sailors' one of five listed in Small Talbotypes 40–45**
SCIENCE MUSEUM, 1 positive: sheet 11.3 × 9.1 cm; image 10.4 × 8.3 cm; negative 9.6 × 7 cm; trimmed after printing, tabs

**PG15 Group of Greeks, one of five listed in Small Talbotypes 40–45.**
SCIENCE MUSEUM, 3 positives: sheet 10.7 × 9.2 cm; image 10.3 × 8.6 cm; negative 10.3 × 8.6 cm; waxed, 3 corners clipped

**PG16 Group of Greeks, one of five listed in Small Talbotypes 40–45.**
SCIENCE MUSEUM, 1 positive: sheet 11 × 9.8 cm; image 10.5 × 8.5 cm; negative 9.6 × 8 cm, trimmed

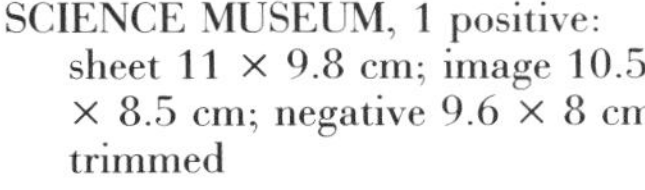

**PG17 Group of Greeks, one of five listed in Small Talbotypes 40–45.**
SCIENCE MUSEUM, 2 positives: sheet 11.5 × 9.8 cm; image 10.7 × 8.6 cm; negative 9.9 × 8 cm, trimmed after printing

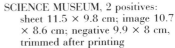

**PG18 'Valetta Pilots' inscribed verso**
SCIENCE MUSEUM, negative 11.3 × 9.3 cm; waxed, tabs

**PG19 Figures standing in front of date palm, Malta**
SCIENCE MUSEUM, negative 16.1 × 20.3 cm; trimmed, waxed

**PG20 Seamen, Ilfracombe, Devon**
SCIENCE MUSEUM, negative: sheet 11.3 × 9.4 cm; image 9.4 × 8.4 cm; waxed, corners clipped, ink on edges, dense

**PG21 Seamen, Ilfracombe, Devon**
SCIENCE MUSEUM, negative: sheet 11.2 × 9.2 cm; image 10.5 × 9; waxed, dense

**PG22 'Bay Pier Ilfracombe' inscribed verso**
SCIENCE MUSEUM, negative: sheet 11.3 × 9.1 cm; image 10.9 × 8.5 cm

**PG23 Man and woman before cactus**
HANS P KRAUS JR COLLECTION, 1 positive: sheet 19.5 × 17.2 cm; image 14.5 × 13.8 cm; watermark, Whatman Turkey Mill 1839

**PG24 Two gentlemen, Malta**
SCIENCE MUSEUM, 2 positives: sheet 10 × 11 cm; image 8.5 × 10 cm; negative 8.5 × 10 cm; waxed, 4 corners clipped

Sotheby's, London, 1 positive: sheet 9 × 11.3 cm; image 8.5 × 10 cm

**PG25 Two gentlemen, Malta**
SCIENCE MUSEUM, 1 positive: sheet 11.2 × 10.7 cm; image 9 × 8.3 cm; negative 8 × 10 cm, trimmed

### *Individual* (PI)

**PI1 Possibly Ann Harriet Jones**
ROYAL PHOTOGRAPHIC SOCIETY, 1 (lower right) of 4 positives on single sheet 25 × 19.6 cm; sheet 9.3 × 11.7 cm; image 8.7 × 11.3 cm

**PI2 '25 Captain Twopenny', listed in Small Talbotypes**
SCIENCE MUSEUM, 2 positives: sheet 11.2 × 9.4 cm; image 10.5 × 8.6 cm; negative 9.2 × 8 cm, trimmed

**PI3 Man in coat and plaid waistcoat**
VICTORIA AND ALBERT MUSEUM Ph 32B–1983, 1 positive: image 6.1 × 9.1 cm, trimmed

**PI4 Man seated in doorway**
VICTORIA AND ALBERT MUSEUM Ph 34–1983, 1 positive: image 21.8 × 16.8 cm, trimmed

**PI5 Gentleman**
VICTORIA AND ALBERT MUSEUM Ph 76–1983, 1 positive: image 8.9 × 10.3 cm, trimmed

**PI6 Gentleman with wicker basket**

VICTORIA AND ALBERT MUSEUM Ph 119–1983, 1 positive: image 8.4 × 10.1 cm, trimmed

**PI7 Man in plaid waistcoat**
VICTORIA AND ALBERT MUSEUM Ph 120–1983, 1 positive: image 7.9 × 10.7 cm, trimmed

## STUDIES (S)

**S1 '4. Study of Canons.' listed in Small Talbotypes**
SCIENCE MUSEUM, negative 9.8 × 8.3 cm; trimmed, waxed

**S2 '48. Wine Cart.' listed in Small Talbotypes**
SCIENCE MUSEUM, 1 positive: sheet 11.4 × 9 cm, image 9.8 × 7.8 cm; negative 9.8 × 7.8 cm, trimmed

**S3 Rock forms**
VICTORIA AND ALBERT MUSEUM Ph 78, 1 positive: image 19 × 16.9 cm, trimmed

**S4 Barrel floats**
VICTORIA AND ALBERT MUSEUM Ph 51–1983, 1 positive: image 22.3 × 18.2 cm, trimmed

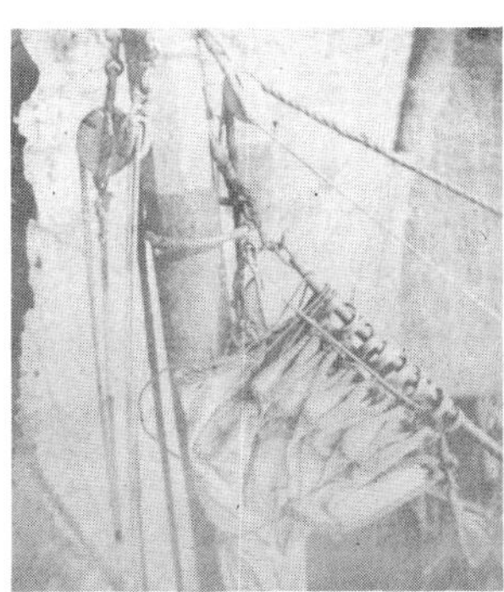

**S5 Furled sail**
VICTORIA AND ALBERT MUSEUM Ph 90–1983, 1 positive: image 10.1 × 8.2 cm; trimmed, faint
Hans P Kraus Jr Collection, 1 positive: image 10.3 × 8.3 cm, trimmed

**S6 Anchor and block**
VICTORIA AND ALBERT MUSEUM Ph 127–1983, 1 positive: image 22.7 × 17.6 cm; trimmed, faint

**S7 Pilings and lines**
SCIENCE MUSEUM, 1 positive: sheet 11.4 × 9.9 cm; image 9.9 × 8 cm, very faint; negative 9.9 × 8 cm

**S8 Garden implements**
VICTORIA AND ALBERT MUSEUM Ph 96–1983, 1 positive: image 15.3 × 20.1 cm

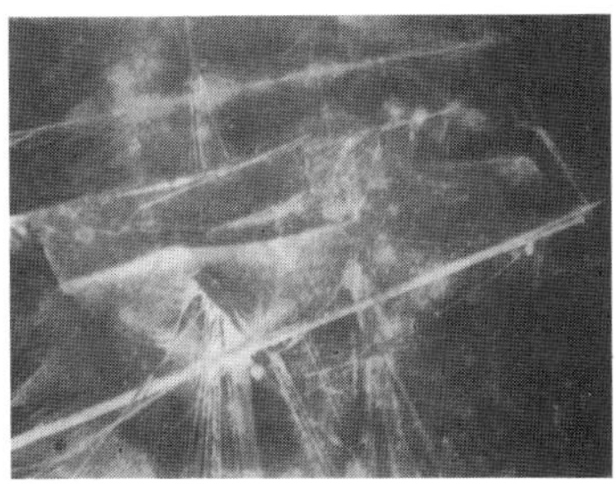

**S9 Mast and Rigging**
HANS P KRAUS JR COLLECTION, negative 21.8 × 18.1 cm

**S10 '8. Old capstan' listed in Small Talbotypes**
SCIENCE MUSEUM, 1 positive: sheet 11.7 × 9.2 cm; image 10.6 × 8.8 cm; negative 9.9 × 8.2 cm, trimmed

**S11 '21. Old capstan' listed in Small Talbotypes**
SCIENCE MUSEUM, negative 9.9 × 7.9 cm

**S12 Leaf (Talbotype positive)**
VICTORIA AND ALBERT MUSEUM Ph 66, plate 20.8 × 16.4 cm (size of leaf 12.2 × 11.4 cm)

**S13 Sea plant (photogenic drawing)**
HANS P KRAUS JR COLLECTION, negative 10.9 × 16.3 cm

**S14 Sea plants (photogenic drawing)**
HANS P KRAUS JR COLLECTION, negative 15.1 × 21.3 cm

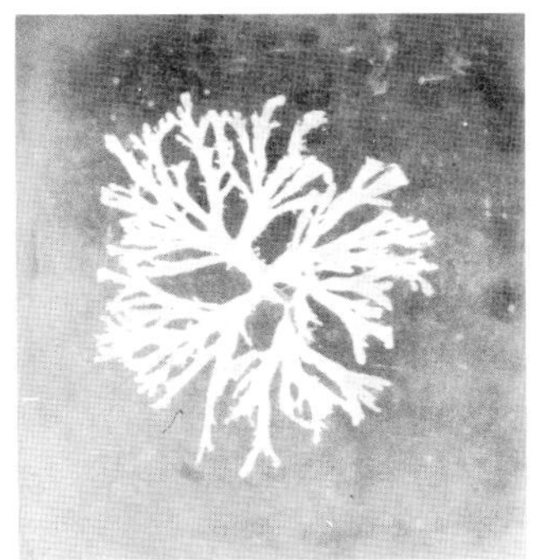

**S15 Sea plant (photogenic drawing)**
HANS P KRAUS JR COLLECTION, negative 21 × 17.8 cm

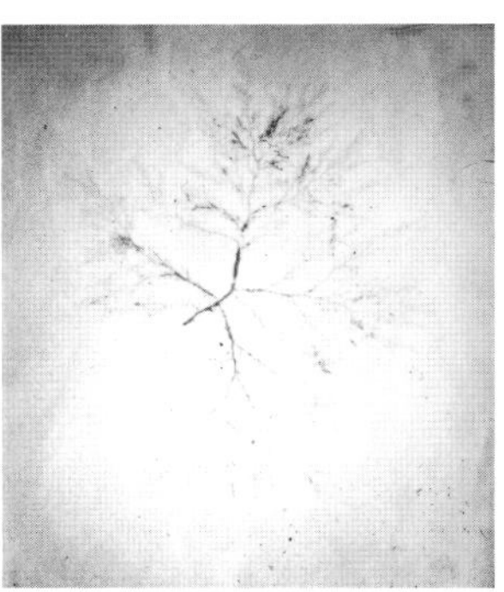

**S16 Sea plant (Talbotype positive)**
HANS P KRAUS JR COLLECTION, positive: 21.6 × 17.5 cm, watermark 'NASH'

## HAND-COLOURED CALOTYPES (H-C)

**H-C1 House of Sallust, Pompeii**
DAVID ALAN BROWN COLLECTION, 21.1 × 16.3 cm watercolour and gouache (see AP 3)

**H-C2 Merchant Street, Valetta, Malta**
ROLLIN AND VIRGINIA BUCKMAN COLLECTION, 16.2 × 20.7 cm watercolour and gouache

**H-C3 Bay of Naples**
ROLLIN AND VIRGINIA BUCKMAN COLLECTION, 19.9 × 14.8 cm watercolour and gouache

# APPENDIX A1:

## *Selected Genealogy*

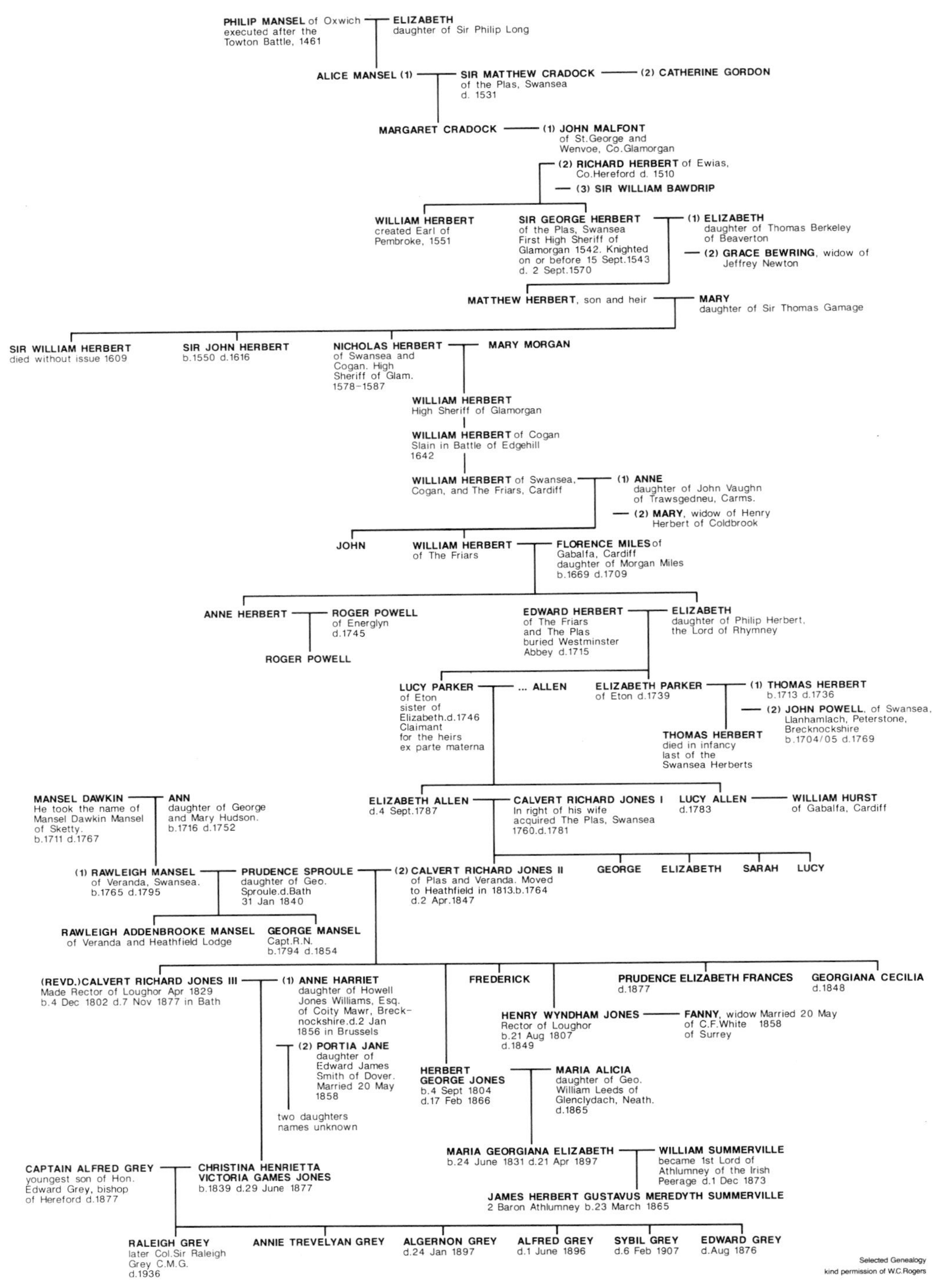

# APPENDIX A2:

## Cambrian *[Swansea], 9 November 1899, p 8*

We have this day to announce the death of the Rev. Calvert Jones, which took place at Bath on Wednesday last, the 7th instant. The gentleman whose decease we now record was born about the year 1804 [*sic*], and had therefore arrived at the boundary commonly assigned to human life. He had been ailing about three weeks previous to his decease, during which time he fell from his chair and broke a rib. The injury then sustained was followed by inflammation of the chest, which was [the] proximate cause of his death. The deceased gentleman did not follow at least in recent times, his profession as a clergyman, but he owned by inheritance the Herbert Chapel of St. Mary's Church, and also one of its aisles. He was a brother of Captain Jones, R.N., a Knight of the Legion of Honour, and of the late Sergeant Jones, one of the Metropolitan County Court judges, and a half-brother of the late Raleigh [*sic*] Mansel, Esq. A few months ago, he lost his only child by a first marriage, who was the wife of Lt. Col. Grey, a son of the Bishop of Hereford, and a nephew of the last Earl Grey. By this marriage there are several children; but it is believed that the Swansea estates pass for life to Lt. Col. Grey. Mr. Jones was educated at Oriel College, Oxford, and was a contemporary with Mr. Talbot of Margam, when Bishop Coplestone was provost of that College, at which college, on taking his degree, he obtained a first class in Mathematics. But he was an early proficient in photography, and was also a skillful artist, painting in oil colours, and an accomplished musician. He married his second wife Miss Portia Smith, and has left two daughters by this marriage surviving him. He and his family were intimately connected with Swansea, being the owners of large property in the town and extensive mineral estates in the neighbourhood. And the people of Swansea are under a deep debt of gratitude to them in consequence of his father having given the ground of our magnificent market – a splendid property now producing 3,000 per annum which the corporation now enjoys. The Rev. Calvert Jones was a magistrate of this County, and a deputy lieutenant.

# APPENDIX A3:
## *'On a Binocular Camera', Calvert Richard Jones (extract from the* Journal of the Photographic Society)





2. Mr. Calvert Jones, "*On a Binocular Camera.*"

(The substance of a communication made to the Photographic Society, May 5th, 1853.)

Although the following paper does not refer exactly to stereoscopic cameras, I think the subject of sufficient importance to warrant my bringing it before the Society at this opportunity.

Having been, ever since the discovery of photography, an ardent follower of the beautiful art, I have long been convinced that the picture comprised in the field of view of an ordinary lens is not extensive enough, does not subtend an angle sufficiently large to satisfy our eyes; it is, in fact, analogous to what we see when we look out at nature with one eye shut.

To obviate this imperfection, I have been constantly in the habit of taking double pictures; *i. e.* having taken an upright view, I move the camera in a small arc till the left-hand side of the second view coincides with the right-hand side of the first.

Such views are, I believe, common enough, and I think that I can appeal to any person whether these kinds of pictures are not, when joined together and mounted, more satisfactory to the eye than any single view.

Of course I speak of general compositions, such as landscapes, architectural subjects, &c., and not of studies of any particular objects, such as figures, groups, or still-life.

However, from the two portions of double pictures being taken on different pieces of paper, and the difficulty of making the edges meet with perfect accuracy, it appears to me a great desideratum that we should be enabled by some means to take the two views on one sheet of paper.

For this purpose, several plans have suggested themselves to me; such as rolling off the first portion of the view when it has been taken; and other devices which I have not found likely to be perfectly successful.

I cannot, however, help thinking that the desired end may possibly be effected by means of a binocular camera; first, taking one view with one lens, and having accurately covered the portion done, by a slide or trap-door, taking the remaining half with the second lens.

I subjoin a sketch of the kind of camera which I would propose to adopt for the above purpose; and throw out the idea to the manufacturers of these instruments, whether it may not be possible to construct the paper-holders with such nicety as to attain the desired accuracy at the junction of the edges.

The size and beauty of the pictures would, I submit, amply repay the outlay of the two lenses required: and I can only add in conclusion, that though I am far from thinking it necessary to have such a camera for all views, I am of opinion that it would form a very useful appendage for taking a more perfect and satisfactory representation of many compositions in nature which cannot be adequately depicted by a single view.

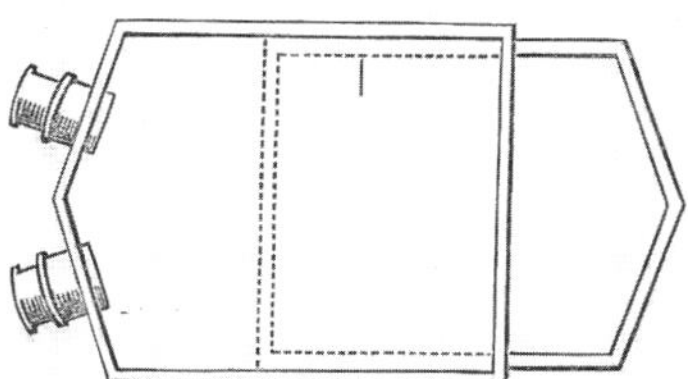

The above is a section of the binocular camera, and the view below a rough idea of its appearance, with one slide up.

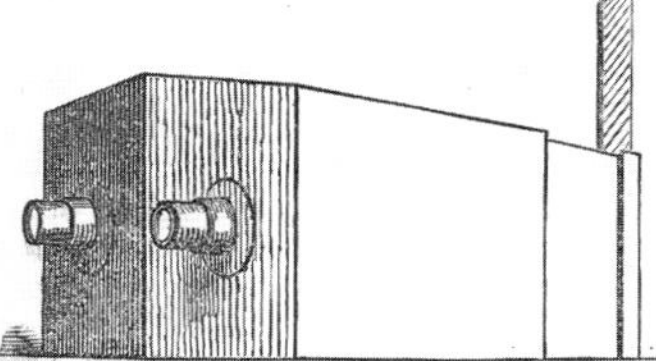

Mr. Harding (to whose opinion Mr. Calvert Jones appealed in the course of his explanations regarding the artistic merits of the double views obtained by his camera) said,—My attention was first called to the subject at Mr. Jones's house, where, to my astonishment, he showed me these pictures; and that you may perfectly understand what is intended by them, I will suppose that we have two pictures—say, one a view taken up the river, the second one taken the other way, and beginning perhaps where the first leaves off. Thus, you observe, there will be two pictures taken of one view. Those pictures afterwards are joined together, and the satisfaction to the eye, in a pictorial point of view, is hardly to be imagined. I was much struck with such specimens as Mr. Jones showed me. I saw clearly what he intended, viz. that when you take a picture in a camera with two lenses to it, you get twice as much as you see with one eye. Unless you had seen specimens of two views taken in this way and joined together, you would have no suspicion of anything but a binocular picture, such as you have been accustomed to see where you have two views of the same spot held to both eyes; but in the way suggested by Mr. Jones, you have a view taken exactly as you see it with both eyes. I believe such gentlemen as are disposed to make experiments, will soon find out how perfectly true this is.

Mr. Shadbolt.—It appears to me that the camera exhibited by Mr. Clark has all the elements which are necessary for constructing views in the manner in which Mr. Jones has illustrated. It would merely require a modification of the sliding arrangement; for, by adapting the parallel ruler apparatus to obtain the particular points, so that you would always have one view at the end of where the other begins, you can overcome the difficulty of joining, by using one piece of paper.

Mr. Calvert Jones.—I propose that it should be done on one piece of paper.

Mr. Shadbolt.—Your idea could be carried out by that very instrument.

3. "*Note on a new portable reflecting Stereoscope,*" by C. Wheatstone, Esq., F.R.S.

The most perfect and generally useful form of the stereoscope is that with reflecting mirrors described in my earliest memoir "On Binocular Vision," published in the Philosophical Transactions for 1838. Pictures of any size may be placed in it, at the proper point of sight, with the proper convergence of the optic axes, and it admits of every requisite adjustment to make the pair of binocular pictures coincide correctly.

I have described in my second memoir a portable stereoscope which folds into a small compass, and which is well suited for pictures not exceeding six inches by four. I have since constructed an instrument, very convenient for carrying about, which is adapted to exhibit pictures of the largest dimensions usually taken, as well as smaller ones, and which may be made use of either for mounted or unmounted pictures. When closed it occupies a space of 9 inches in length, 5 in breadth, and $4\frac{1}{2}$ in height; when expanded the instrument is 2 feet in length, 1 foot in height, and 9 inches in depth. The base and sides consist of jointed bars on the principle of the lazy-tongs; the two mirrors fold together back to back, and, by means of a hinge on their support, fall into a groove on the base fitted to receive them. On the top of each of the expanding sides a clip 9 inches in length receives the picture (which there is no need to mount on card-board) and holds it by the pressure of a suitably disposed spring; and a similar but detached spring clip is applied to the lower end of the picture in order to keep it flat and in a vertical position.

The pictures being fixed in the clips, so that their reflected images shall appear single and coincide in all their parts, the accurate adjustment to the sight of different persons is effected by sliding to and fro the pillar which supports the mirrors; the optic axes being caused to

From the *Journal of the Photographic Society*, vol. 1, 1854, pp 60–1.

# APPENDIX A4:

## *Small Talbotypes*

Small Talbotypes.

1. Boat on the marine.
2. In Vittoriosa.
3. Maltese Caleche.
4. Study of Canons.
5. Capstan on the marine.
6. Felucca hauled up.
7. Boats at Senglea.
8. Old Capstan.
9. On the marine.
10. Strada Marsa Muscetto.
11. Boat ashore.
11. bis. Do (joins to it).
12. Strada Marsa Muscetto.
13. Heaving down. Capstan.
14. Boats ashore.
15. Do
16. Strada Marsa Muscetto.
17. Strada Molini a Vento.
18. Piazza Regina.
19. Fishing boats ashore.
20. Windows.
21. Old Capstan.
22. New Victualling Office.
23. Family group.
24. Do
25. Captn Twopenny.
26. Piazza Vittoriosa.
27. On the marine. Valetta.
27. bis. (joins on to it).
28. Fishing boats. Senglea.
29. Do.
30. Piazza Regina.
31. Piazza S. Giorgio.
32. Do
33. Strada Marsa Muscetto (bad paper)
34. Windmill
35. Do
36. Part of do.
37. Strada Marsa Muscetto. (bad paper)
38. Piazza Vittoriosa.
39. Strada Vescovo. (bad paper)
40. Group of Greeks.
41. Do
42. Do
43. Do
44. Do
45. Do
46. On the marine.
47. Piazza Vittoriosa.
48. Wine cart.
49. Albergo di Castile.

List of 'Small Talbotypes' in Calvert Jones's hand. Undated but probably 1846–7.

# APPENDIX B:

## *Drawings and Paintings by Calvert Richard Jones*

1 An officer of the 15th Hussars. Inscribed '15 Hussars, 1835'. (17.8 × 26.1 cm; *Martyn Gregory Gallery*)

2 The brig 'Hardy' under sail. Inscribed 'Hardy of Marblehead' and dated 'Aug 22 1834'. (26.7 × 17.8 cm; *Martyn Gregory Gallery*)

3 Beached fishing boats, 'Calvert R Jones 1840'. (*Martyn Gregory Gallery*)

4 Rheola House near Neath. Inscribed in ink 'Rheola' and in pencil 'Hills at the right', and dated 'May 19 1836'. (*Martyn Gregory Gallery*)

5 The Custom House, Dublin, from the south-east. Inscribed 'Dublin' and dated 'Jan 9 1836'; pen and ink and watercolours. (26.8 × 17.8 cm; *Buckman Collection*)

6 ‘Calvert R Jones and Family and Dog and Swansea Pilot Boat S10 Beached’. Two studies. (25.1 × 17.8 cm; *Glynn Vivian Art Gallery, Swansea*)

7 Firing practice. Pencil heightened with white. (24.8 × 17.8 cm; *Colin Lacy Gallery*)

8 Three gondoliers: a study. Pencil and wash drawing. (24.8 × 17.8 cm; *Colin Lacy Gallery*)

9 'Calvert R Jones and Family and dog. Sept 7th 1846'. Two studies, pencil heightened with white. (24.8 × 17.8 cm; *Dr Roderick G Howell Collection*)

10 Inscribed 'August 4th, 1846'. (24.2 × 17.8 cm; *Colin Lacy Gallery*)

11 Coastal shipping: Swansea schooner under sail. Oil painting. (71.2 × 50.8 cm; *Glynn Vivian Art Gallery, Swansea*)

12 Inscribed 'H.M.S. Dido. Dec. 2. 1856'. Pencil and wash drawing. (27.0 × 20.0 cm; *Colin Lacy Gallery*)

13 Shipping in harbour. (26.8 × 19.7 cm; *Colin Lacy Gallery*)

14 Ballast boat: Mediterranean. Pencil. (26.8 × 19.7; *Colin Lacy Gallery*)

15 Ferry: treadmill construction. Pencil. (26.8 × 19.7 cm; *Colin Lacy Gallery*)

# BIBLIOGRAPHY


Arnold, H J P, *William Henry Fox Talbot, Pioneer of Photography and Man of Science*, London, Hutchinson Benham Ltd, 1977

Boase, T S R, *English Art 1800–1870*, Oxford, Clarendon Press, 1959

Booth, Mark Haworth, ed, *The Golden Age of British Photography 1839–1900*, New York, Aperature, 1984

Brettell, Richard R, *et al*, *Paper and Light. The Calotype in France and Great Britain 1839–1870*, Boston, David R Godine, 1984

Buckland, Gail, *Fox Talbot and the Invention of Photography*, Boston, David R Godine, 1980

Gernsheim, Helmut & Alison, *L J M Daguerre*, 2nd rev. edn, New York, Dover Publications Ltd, 1968

Hardie, Martin, *Water-Colour Painting in Britain. Vol. I, The Eighteenth Century*, London, William Clowes and Sons Ltd, 1966

*Water-Colour Painting in Britain. Vol II, The Romantic Period*, London, B T Batsford Ltd, 1967

Howell, Dr R G, *Under Sail*, Swansea, Glynn Vivian Art Gallery, 1987

'The Rev. Calvert Jones as an Artist' (unpublished)

Hughes, John Vivian, *The Wealthiest Commoner: C.R.M. Talbot*, Port Talbot, Talbot Printing Co Ltd, 1978

*Margam Castle*, Port Talbot, Talbot Printing Co Ltd, 1981

Jammes, Andre & Janis, Eugenie Parry, *The Art of French Calotype*, Princeton, New Jersey, Princeton University Press, 1983

Kraus, Hans P Jr, *Sun Pictures*, Four Catalogues, New York, Hans P Kraus Jr Inc

Lassam, Robert E & Grey, Michael, *The Romantic Era: La Calotipia in Italia 1845–1860*, Firenze, Fratelli Alinari, 1988

Ostroff, Eugene, 'The Calotype and the Photographer', *The Journal of Photographic Science*, Vol 26, No 1, January/February 1978

Painting, David, *Swansea's Place in the History of Photography*, Swansea, Royal Institution of South Wales, 1982

Rogers, W C, *A Pictorial History of Swansea*, Llandysul, Wales, Gomer Press, 1981

'Jones of the Plas, Verandah [*sic*], and Heathfield Lodge, Swansea' (unpublished)

Thomas, D B, *The First Negatives*, London, HMSO, 1964

Thornthwaite, William Henry, *Photographic Manipulation*, London, Edward Palmer, 1843

Ward, John & Stevenson, Sara, *Printed Light*, Edinburgh, HMSO, 1986

# INDEX

References are to page numbers, except in entries for titles of plates, where the plate number is given.

Page numbers referring to illustrations in the main text are italicized. Pages in the catalogue section are indicated by '(C)', and those in the appendices by '(A)'. Footnotes are shown by 'n'.

The catalogue section is indexed by its subject groups, e.g. 'marine subjects', not by the titles of the individual items.

Printed in the United Kingdom for Her Majesty's Stationery Office
Dd. 289379 C20 1/90 36145